PROBLEMS IN
UNDERGRADUATE PHYSICS

VOLUME I

MECHANICS

PROBLEMS IN UNDERGRADUATE PHYSICS

VOLUME I
MECHANICS

BY

S. P. STRELKOV, I. A. YAKOVLEV

TRANSLATED BY
D. E. BROWN

TRANSLATION EDITED BY
D. ter HAAR

PERGAMON PRESS
OXFORD · LONDON · EDINBURGH · NEW YORK
PARIS · FRANKFURT

Pergamon Press Ltd., Headington Hill Hall, Oxford
4 & 5 Fitzroy Square, London W. 1

Pergamon Press (Scotland) Ltd., 2 & 3 Teviot Place, Edinburgh 1

Pergamon Press Inc., 122 East 55th St., New York 22, N.Y.

Pergamon Press GmbH, Kaiserstrasse 75, Frankfurt-am-Main

First edition 1965

This translation corresponds to the Russian book
Сборник задач по общему курсу физики, часть I
(third edition) published by Nauka, Moscow, 1964, and
includes amendments and additions supplied by the
authors during the course of the translation.

CONTENTS

50651

PREFACE

THIS set of four books of problems is based on a translation of a Russian collection which has been in use by students in physics at Moscow State University for a number of years. Where appropriate, answers and solutions to the problems are given in the second part of each volume.

During the course of the translation of these volumes, the authors provided a large list of amendments and additions to their Russian text and these have all been incorporated in this English edition. Many of the additional problems are on topics which have developed during recent years.

The standard of the problems is roughly equivalent to an undergraduate course in physics at a British or at an American university; it varies from the simple to the rather sophisticated. They can be used in conjunction with almost any textbook on physics at the appropriate level.

D. TER HAAR

PROBLEMS

§ 1. KINEMATICS

1. A boat rowed across a river has a speed of 2 m sec^{-1} relative to the water, in a direction perpendicular to the flow. The speed of the flow is 1 m sec^{-1}. Find the total speed v of the boat and the direction of this vector relative to the river banks.

2. Two ferry landing-stages are situated opposite one another on the banks of a river, the speed of flow of which is 0·5 m sec^{-1}. What course should a ferry-boat take in order to cross the river along the straight line from one landing-stage to the other? In these conditions, what is the speed v_1 with which the ferry-boat will cross the river, given that the speed it develops relative to the water is 0·8 m sec^{-1}?

3. A tube is mounted on a flat cart which is in uniform motion on a horizontal plane. How must the tube be orientated on the cart in order for rain drops, falling vertically, to miss hitting the walls when falling inside the tube? The motion of the rain drops is assumed uniform.

4. A ship travels westwards with a speed of 6·5 m sec^{-1}. A wind is blowing from the south-west with a speed of 3·5 m sec^{-1}. What will be the wind speed v recorded by the device on the ship? What will be the wind direction found by these devices relative to the course of the ship?

5. Two aeroplanes are flying simultaneously from a given point in mutually perpendicular directions. The speed of one is $v_1 = 300$ km hr^{-1}, of the other $v_2 = 400$ km hr^{-1}. How does the distance between the aeroplanes increase with time? What will this distance S be at the instant when the first aeroplane has flown a distance $S_1 = 900$ km?

3

6. Two ships are travelling parallel to each other in opposite directions with speeds v_1 and v_2. One ship fires on the other. At what angle φ should the gun be aimed at the target ship in order to make a hit, if the shot is fired at the instant when both vessels are on the straight line perpendicular to their course? The shell velocity v_0 is assumed constant.

7. A cutter travels between two points on a river at a distance $L = 100$ km from one another. The journey takes $t_1 = 4$ hr with the current, and $t_2 = 10$ hr against the current. Find the speed v_1 of the current and the speed v_2 of the cutter relative to the water.

8. A fisherman is sailing up-stream; when passing under a bridge, he drops a boat-hook in the water. After half an hour he discovers this, turns back, and overtakes the boat-hook 5 km below the bridge. What is the speed of the current if the fisherman rows at the same speed up and down the river?

9. Two trains are travelling in opposite directions with speeds v_1, v_2 respectively. An object is thrown horizontally and perpendicularly to the diretion of motion with a speed v_0 (which can be assumed constant throughout) from the first train on to the platform of the second. (1) What is the angle φ_1 to the direction of the rails formed by the projection of the moving object on to the road-bed? (2) What angle φ_2 will be made with the edge of the platform of the second train, parallel to its motion, by the projection of the moving object on to the platform? (3) What are the speeds of the object relative to the road-bed (v') and relative to the platform (v'')?

10. A right-angle is drawn on a sheet of paper. A ruler, which always remains perpendicular to the bisectrix of this angle, moves over the paper with a speed 10 cm sec^{-1}. The ends of the ruler intersect the sides of the angle. What are the speeds along the sides of the angle of their points of intersection with the ruler?

11. A photographer, at a distance l from a railway track, wants to photograph a train travelling at a speed v, at the instant when his line of vision to the train makes an angle α with the track. What maximum exposure t_{max} can the photographer give if the permissible blurring of the image on the plate must not exceed d, and the focal length of the camera lens is f?

12. A body moving with constant acceleration travels consecutively over two equal 10 m segments of its path S. Find the acceleration a of the body and its speed v_0 at the start of the first segment, if the first segment is traversed in time $t_1 = 1 \cdot 06$ sec and the second in $t_2 = 2 \cdot 2$ sec.

13. Draw the graphs of the speeds and paths as functions of time, if the graphs of the acceleration of certain bodies are as shown in Fig. 1 (the initial speed of the bodies is always zero). *

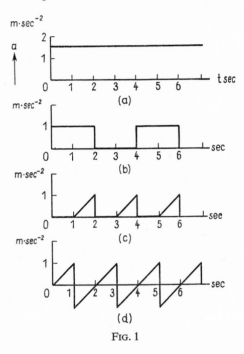

Fig. 1

14. Draw the graphs of the acceleration and path as functions of time, if the speed of a body is as shown in Fig. 2 (as a function of time). (Cf. the footnote to Problem 13.)

15. What is the permissible limiting landing speed v of a parachutist, if a man can safely jump from a height $h = 2$ m?

---

* The accelerations are schematised as functions of time on these graphs, i. e., it is assumed that the acceleration changes with a jump at certain instants. This is done to simplify the problems. An acceleration can in fact change very rapidly, though never with a jump, i.e., it must be a continuous function of time. The assumption of jump-type accelerations is equivalent to the graphs of the velocities having breaks. Similar remarks apply to Problem 14.

16. Two bodies are thrown simultaneously from a tower with the same initial speed v_0: one vertically upwards, the other vertically downwards. How will the distance S between the bodies vary with time? (Air resistance is neglected.)

17. What initial velocity v_0 should a signal rocket have, if it is shot at an angle of 45° to the horizontal and is to flare up at its highest point, assuming that its ignition time is 6 sec? (Air resistance to the motion of the rocket is neglected.)

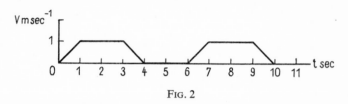

FIG. 2

18. At what point of the trajectory of a body, thrown at an angle to the horizontal, will the acceleration normal to the trajectory be a maximum? (Air resistance is neglected.)

19. A shot is fired from an artillery gun at an angle φ to the horizontal. The initial speed of the shell is v_0. Investigate analytically the motion of the shell, neglecting air resistance and the curvature of the earth's surface. Illustrate graphically the functional relationships obtained.

(1) Find the vertical and horizontal components of the velocity vector v and the absolute value of the velocity as a function of time.

(2) Find the time of flight of the shell from the gun to the point where it reaches the earth.

(3) Find the angle α between the velocity vector and the horizontal as a function of time.

(4) Find the Cartesian coordinates (the x-axis is horizontal and the y-axis vertical) of the shell as functions of time.

(5) Find the equation of the shell's trajectory $y = f(x)$ and, using this equation, draw the trajectory.

(6) Find the maximum height H_{max} of the shell above the earth.

(7) Find the horizontal range L of the shell as a function of its initial velocity and the firing angle. At what firing angle φ^* will the range be maximum for a given initial velocity of the shell?

20. Draw the graph of the curve formed by the ends of the velocity vectors of a shell fired at an angle φ to the horizontal, assuming that all these vectors, which correspond to the shell velocity at different instants, are drawn from the same point. This graph is called the *hodograph* of the velocity vector. (Air resistance is neglected.)

21. Jets of water flow at angles 60, 45 and 30° respectively from three pipes located at ground level. Find the ratio of the maximum heights h reached by the jets from each pipe, and the ratio of the ranges L over the ground. (Air resistance to the flow of the jets is neglected.)

22. What is the maximum range L of a hammer thrown with initial velocity 20 msec^{-1} in a gymnasium of height 8 m? In this case, what must be the angle φ between the floor and the initial velocity vector of the hammer? Assume that the height above the floor of the initial point of the hammer's trajectory is small compared with the height of the gymnasium. The hammer must never strike the ceiling in its travel. (Air resistance is neglected.)

23. A shell is fired vertically upwards with an initial velocity v_0 from the deck of a ship travelling at a speed v_1. Neglecting air resistance, find the magnitude and direction of the velocity vector v of the shell as functions of time and the equation of the trajectory of the shell in a fixed coordinate system. (The results of Problem 19 can be used to simplify the solution.)

24. Find by the analytic method of investigating motions as applied in Problems 19 and 23 the trajectory, velocity v and acceleration a of a body whose coordinates are the following functions of time: $x = ct^2$, $y = bt^2$.

25. An aeroplane flies horizontally along a straight course with speed v. The pilot has to drop a bomb on a target lying ahead of the plane. At what angle to the vertical must he see the target at the instant of dropping the bomb? At this instant, what is the distance from the target to the point immediately below the aeroplane? (The air resistance to the bomb is neglected.)

26. The speed of a bullet can be found from its distance Δh below the horizontal at a given range L. The drop Δh in the trajectory is determined from the holes made by the bullet in two vertical screens, arranged one behind the other in the path of the bullet (A and B in

Fig. 3). Find the speed of the bullet on the assumption that Δh and L are known and that the air resistance is negligible.

27. A target situated on a hill can be seen from the site of a gun at an angle α above the horizontal. The range (distance along the horizontal from the gun to the target) is L. If the shell is fired at angle β, find the initial velocity required for it to strike the target. (The air resistance is neglected.)

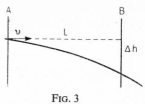

FIG. 3

28. Loads start to slide without friction simultaneously from the top end of the vertical diameter of a circle along grooves which occupy different chords of the circle. Show that all the loads arrive at the circle at the same time.

29. A material particle slips without friction down a curve of arbitrary slope. Show that, after descending a depth h, its velocity is the same as if it had fallen freely a distance h.

30. Balls are thrown in all directions with the same speeds from a tower. Show that, in the absence of air resistance, the centres of all the balls lie on a sphere, the centre of which drops with the acceleration of a freely falling body, whilst its radius is $v_0 t$, where v_0 is the initial speed of the balls, and t is the time from the instant when they are thrown.

31. A truck has to convey a load in the shortest time from one point to another at a distance L. It can only start up or slow down its motion with the same constant acceleration a, then pass to a state of uniform motion or else come to rest. What maximum speed must the truck attain in order to satisfy the above-mentioned requirement?

32. A boat whose speed is v_0 drops its sail at the instant t_0 but continues to move. Measurements of the boat's speed carried out during this motion show a hyperbolic dependence of the speed on time. Show that the acceleration a of the boat is proportional to the square of its speed.

33. Use the conditions of the previous problem to find the following functions: (1) the distance S travelled by the boat as a function of time t and (2) the speed v of the boat as a function of the distance travelled after dropping the sail.

34. A shell is fired horizontally forwards with a speed v_s from a gun mounted on an aeroplane flying horizontally with speed v_a. Neglecting air resistance, find: (1) the equation of the shell's trajectory relative to the earth, (2) the equation of the shell's trajectory to the aeroplane, (3) the equation of the trajectory of the aeroplane relative to the shell.

35. A boat crosses a river with a constant velocity v relative to the water, perpendicular to the current. The width of the river is d and the speed of the current is zero at the banks and increases linearly as the centre of the river is approached, at which point its value is u. Find the trajectory of the boat, and the distance x_0 that it goes down along the current, from the point where it leaves one bank to the point where it reaches the other.

36. Solve the previous problem on the assumption that the speed of the current increases from one bank to the centre of the river according to the parabolic law $v_x = ky^2$.

37. A particle moves uniformly along the plane trajectory illustrated in Fig. 4. At what point is the acceleration of the particle a maximum?

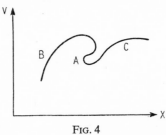

Fig. 4

38. The moon revolves round the earth with a period $T = 27$ days. The mean radius of the moon's orbit is $R = 4 \times 10^5$ km. Find the linear velocity v of the moon round the earth and its normal acceleration a.

39. What are the graphs of the absolute values of the speed and acceleration as functions of time for a particle moving uniformly round a circle?

40. Find the mean angular velocity of the third Soviet sputnik, if the period of its rotation in orbit round the earth was 105 min on 6 July 1958.

41. Find the mean linear orbital velocity of the sputnik if its period of rotation in orbit was 105 min and its mean height 1200 km.

42. Use the data regarding the sputnik given in the previous problem to find the mean value of its normal acceleration in orbit.

43. Find the linear velocity v of a point on the earth's surface on the geographical latitude φ, produced by the diurnal rotation of the earth about its axis. The radius of the terrestrial sphere is $R \approx 6400$ km.

44. Find the linear velocity of the earth produced by its original motion. The mean radius of the earth's orbit is $\approx 1 \cdot 5 \times 10^8$ km.

45. Find the normal acceleration of a point on the earth's surface produced by the diurnal rotation of the earth. Find the projection of this acceleration on the direction of the earth's radius at that point. Estimate the values of these quantities for the latitude of Moscow (55° northern latitude). The earth's radius $R \approx 6400$ km.

46. The armature of an electric motor revolves at N revolutions per second; it slows down at a constant rate after switching off the current and comes to rest after n revolutions. Find the angular acceleration of the armature after switching off the current.

47. A car is travelling at 60 km hr^{-1}. How many revolutions per second are made by its wheels if they roll over the road without slipping and the outer diameter of the tyres is 60 cm.

48. Given the conditions of the previous problem, find the normal acceleration of the outer tread of the car tyres.

49. A rope that unwinds without slipping from a rotating shaft carries a bucket that drops into a well with an acceleration 1 m sec^{-2}. What is the angular acceleration of the shaft? How does the angle of rotation of the shaft depend on time? The shaft radius is 25 cm.

50. A car travelling at 40 km hr^{-1} reaches a bend in the road with a radius of curvature of 200 m. The driver brakes the machine on the bend and gives it a deceleration of 0·3 m sec^{-2}. Find the normal and total accelerations of the car on the bend. What is the direction of the total acceleration vector a_{tot} relative to the radius of curvature R of the bend?

51. A wheel of radius R rolls without slip on a horizontal road with velocity v_0 (Fig. 5). Find the horizontal component v_x of the linear velocity of any given point of the circumference of the wheel, the vertical component v_y of this velocity and the modulus of the total velocity of the point. Find the angle α between the total velocity vector of a point on the circumference and the direction of the progressive motion of its axis. Show that the direction of the total velocity vector of a point A on the circumference is always perpendicular to the straight line AB and passes through the highest point of the rolling wheel. Show that, for the point A, $v_{tot} = BA\omega$. Draw the graph of the velocity distribution for all points on a vertical diameter (at a given instant) of the rolling wheel.

Express all the required quantities in terms of v_0, R and the angle φ, formed by the upper vertical radius of the wheel and the radius drawn from the centre O of the wheel to the point A of the circumference.

Hint: The motion of a point of the circumference can be regarded as the sum of two motions: the progressive motion with velocity v_0 of the axis of the wheel and the rotation about this axis. For such a point, in the absence of slip, the modulus of the velocity vector of the progressive motion is equal to the modulus of the linear velocity due to the rotation.

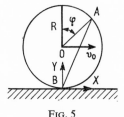

FIG. 5

52. Use the general results obtained in Problem 51 to find the magnitude and direction of the velocity vectors v_1 for two points of the circumference of the wheel, situated at a given instant at opposite ends of a horizontal diameter of the wheel. What are the directions of the accelerations of these two points?

53. A wheel of radius R rolls uniformly without slip along a horizontal path with velocity v. Find the coordinates x and y of any given point A on the circumference of the wheel, expressed as functions of time t or of the angle of rotation of the wheel φ, on the assumption that $\varphi = 0$, $x = 0$, $y = 0$ at $t = 0$ (Fig. 6). Use the expressions obtained for x and y to draw the graph of the trajectory of a point on the circumference.

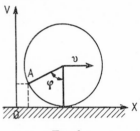

FIG. 6

54. Use the expression for the total velocity of a point on the circumference of a rolling wheel (see Problems 51 and 53) to find the total path traversed by the point between its two successive contacts with the road.

55. A car with wheels of radius R moves with velocity v along a horizontal road, where $v^2 > Rg$ and g is the acceleration due to gravity. What is the maximum height h to which dirt picked up by the wheels can be thrown? Find the point on the tyre from which dirt will be thrown up highest for a given speed of the car. Neglect air resistance to the movement of the dirt through the air.

56. Use the rolling conditions for a wheel described in Problem 51, and the results of its solution, to find the horizontal and vertical components of the acceleration vector of an arbitrary point on the circumference. Give the magnitude and direction of the total acceleration vector for a point of the circumference.

57. An idea of the magnitude and direction of the total acceleration vector in the case of an accelerated rotation (for instance, for a point on the armature of an electric motor) can be obtained by considering the following problem.

A point moves over the circumference of a circle of radius R with constant tangential acceleration a_t, but without initial velocity.

Find the normal and total accelerations of the point, expressed as (1) functions of time t and the acceleration a_t; (2) as functions of the angular acceleration α and the angle of rotation φ of the radius vector of the point from its initial position. Find the angle β between the direction of the total acceleration vector of the point and its radius vector.

58. A cinematograph operator is taking a picture of a descending aircraft through a telephoto lens; at a given instant he turns his camera about the vertical axis with angular velocity ω_1 and about the horizontal with angular velocity $\omega_2 = \omega_1/5$. What is the axis of the rotation which is equivalent to the sum of these two rotations? What angular velocity about this axis is needed to replace the two original rotations?

59. A rigid body rotates simultaneously with angular velocities $\omega_1, \omega_2 = 2\omega_1, \omega_3 = 3\omega_1$ about three mutually perpendicular axes passing through the same point. Find the orientation with respect to these three axes of a single axis, such that rotation about it can replace the three independent rotations. What is the angular velocity with which the body must now rotate about the new axis?

60. A horizontal disc rotates with angular velocity ω_1 about a vertical axis. Another disc, also with a vertical axis, is mounted on the first disc at a distance R from its axis of rotation. The second disc rotates about its axis in the same direction as the first disc, but with angular velocity ω_2. Where is the instantaneous axis of rotation situated, such that rotation of the second disc about it is equivalent to its part in the two rotations with angular velocities ω_1 and ω_2 described above. With what angular velocity ω must the second disc rotate about this instantaneous axis?

61. The rotation of a car engine is transmitted to the drive wheels via the differential — a device that enables the two wheels to rotate with different velocities. Why is a differential necessary? Why cannot the two drive wheels be rigidly fixed to the same axis, to which the engine rotation is transmitted?

62. On the basis of general considerations regarding the motion of a car along a curved path, developed from the previous problem, calculate the velocities of the wheels on a bend. A car with 1·2 m track and wheel radius $r = 30$ cm moves round a bend in the road with radius of curvature $R = 50$ m. The speed of the centre of the car is 36 km hr^{-1}. Find the linear speeds v_i and v_0 of the inner and outer wheels of the car. (Seen from the centre of curvature of the road.)

63. A horizontal disc rotates uniformly with angular velocity ω. A vertical stick is mounted at a distance R from the centre of the disc. Find the law of motion of the shadow of the stick on a vertical screen, if the entire device is illuminated by a horizontal parallel beam. Use this law of motion to draw the graph of the path, velocity and acceleration of the shadow on the screen as functions of time.

§ 2. DYNAMICS OF PARTICLE MOTION ALONG A STRAIGHT LINE AND ELEMENTARY SYSTEMS

64. A mass of 1 kg hangs from a spring balance mounted in a lift. What will the balance indicate if the lift: (1) moves upwards with acceleration $4\cdot9 \text{ m sec}^{-2}$, directed downwards; (2) moves downwards with acceleration $4\cdot9 \text{ m sec}^{-2}$, directed upwards; (3) moves downwards, with acceleration 1 m sec^{-2} directed downwards?

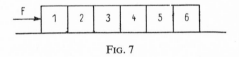

FIG. 7

65. Six equal cubes of mass $m = 1$ kg lie on a smooth horizontal table. A constant force $F = 1$ kg acts on the first cube in the direction indicated by the arrow (Fig. 7). Find the resultant force f acting on each cube. Indicate by arrows on a sketch the forces acting on adjacent faces of each pair of cubes. With what force f does the fourth cube act on the fifth?

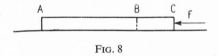

FIG. 8

66. A uniform rod AC of mass m and length l (Fig. 8) is placed on a smooth horizontal table. A constant force F pushes the right-hand end of the rod. What is the force F_1 with which the imaginary segment $AB = 4l/5$ of the rod acts on the segment BC?

67. A body of mass M is placed on a smooth horizontal plane (Fig. 9). Another mass m is suspended from a string passing over a pulley and attached to the mass M. Find the accelerations of the masses M and m and the tension in the string. Neglect the friction of the mass M on the plane and the friction in the pulley, also the masses of the pulley and string.

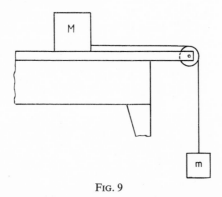

FIG. 9

68. We return to the device described in the previous problem (Fig. 9). (1) We intersect the body of mass M with an imaginary horizontal plane at half its height. What force does the upper half of the mass exert on the lower half? (2) We imaginarily intersect the mass M with a vertical plane through half its length (perpendicular to the plane of the sketch). What force does the left-hand half of the body exert on the right-hand half?

69. In a device similar to that described in Problem 67, three masses m_1, m_2 and m_3 are located on a table and are connected together by strings, and also, via a string over a pulley, to a mass M (Fig. 10). (1) Find the acceleration a of the system; (2) find the tensions in all the strings, on the same assumptions as in Problem 67.

70. A body slides on a plane inclined at an angle α. The friction force between the body and the plane is proportional to the normal pressure force on the plane and is independent of the speed of the body. The coefficient of friction between the surfaces of the body and plane is k. Find the acceleration a with which the body slides.

71. Two identical bodies are joined by a string and lie on a smooth horizontal table, so that the string forms a straight line

(Fig. 11). The string can withstand a tension not exceeding 2 kg. What horizontal force F must be applied to one of the bodies in order to break the string?

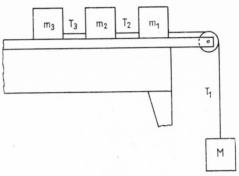

FIG. 10

72. Given the conditions of the previous problem, does the force needed to break the string change if friction is present between the bodies and the table and the coefficient of friction is the same for both bodies?

FIG. 11

73. Two plates of masses m_1, m_2 are joined by a spring (Fig. 12). What force must be applied to the upper plate in order for it to raise the lower plate when it bounces up after the action of the force has ceased? Neglect the mass of the spring.

74. A board lies horizontally on two supports under its ends. A body at rest lies at the middle of the board. What forces act on this body? What forces act on the board and the supports? (The weight of the board itself can be neglected when considering these questions.)

75. A man stands on the board described in the previous problem. He suddenly squats down. What happens in the first instant: does the bending of the board increase or decrease? What happens if the man was sqatting and suddenly gets up?

76. A horse pulls a sledge uniformly. Consider the interaction between the three forces: of the horse, the sledge and the earth's surface. Draw the vectors of the forces acting on each of the three bodies separately, and establish the relationship between them.

77. How does the relationship between the forces change in the example of the previous problem if the horse and sledge move with acceleration a? Find the magnitudes of all the forces if $a = 20\,\mathrm{m\,sec^{-2}}$. The mass of the sledge plus load is $M = 0.5$ tons, the mass of the horse $m = 0.35$ tons, and the coefficient of friction of the sledge on the snow 0.2.

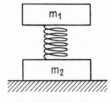

FIG. 12

78. What must the minimum coefficient of friction k be between the tyres of the drive wheels of a car and the road, if the car, with weight $2T$ and load $4T$, has an acceleration $a = 0.2\,\mathrm{m\,sec^{-2}}$?

Consider the problem for two cases: (1) all the wheels are driven; (2) only the rear wheels are driven; assume that the centre of gravity of the car lies at the mid-point between its wheel axes, and the centre of gravity of the load above the rear axle.

79. A load lies on a horizontal board. The coefficient of friction between the board and load is 0.1. What horizontal acceleration must be communicated to the board in order for the load to slide along it?

80. A board of mass $M = 1$ kg lies on a table, and a weight of 2 kg on the board. What force F must be applied to the board in order for it to be slipped out from under the load? The coefficient of friction between the load and board is 0.25, and between the board and table 0.5.

81. A balloon of mass M drops at constant speed. How much ballast ΔM must be thrown out in order for the balloon to start to climb with the same speed? Assume that the lifting force P of the balloon is constant.

82. A pendulum of mass m hangs from a support fixed to a trolley (Fig. 13). Find the direction of the string of the pendulum, i.e. its angle α with the vertical, and its tension T in the following cases: (1) the trolley moves uniformly on a horizontal plane; (2) the trolley moves horizontally with acceleration a; (3) the trolley rolls freely down an inclined plane at an angle φ to the horizontal; (4) the trolley rolls up the plane with acceleration b directed along the plane; (5) the trolley rolls down the plane with the same acceleration b.

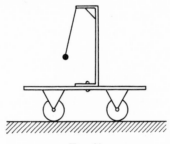

Fig. 13

83. A stone is thrown vertically upwards. At what points of the trajectory does the stone have its maximum acceleration? Consider two cases: (1) air resistance is absent; (2) the air resistance increases with the speed of the stone.

84. What is the direction of the acceleration of an artillery shell after it leaves the barrel of the gun, if air resistance is absent? How does this direction change in the presence of air resistance?

85. A load A of mass m is fixed on springs in a shell fired vertically upwards (Fig. 14). What will be the force exerted by the springs on the load when the shell is rising and falling? Consider the problem, first neglecting, then taking account of air resistance to the motion of the shell.

86. An elementary device for verifying the laws of uniformly accelerated motion can be represented schematically thus: two unequal weights m_1 and m_2 are supported on a string passing over a pulley A (Fig. 15). Find the acceleration of the masses, the tension of the string T and the force f acting on the axis of the pulley of this device. The weights of the string and pulley are neglected, as is the friction at the pulley axis.

87. A string passes round a pulley at the top edge of a smooth, inclined plane (Fig. 16). A load of mass m_1 is attached to one end of the string and lies on the plane. A load of mass m_2 is suspended from the other end. What is the acceleration a of the loads and what is the string tension T? The inclined plane is at an angle α to the horizontal.

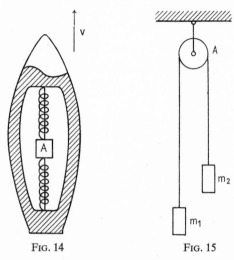

FIG. 14   FIG. 15

88. Masses m_1, m_2 move in the device described in Problem 86. In a time t from the start of the motion the mass m_1 has dropped $1/n$ of the distance that it would have dropped if falling freely. Find the ratio of m_1 to m_2.

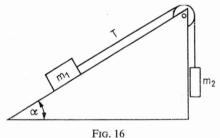

FIG. 16

89. The two weights on either side of the pulley in the device described in Problem 86 are both of mass $m = 250$ g. An additional load $\Delta m = 5$ g is placed on one of the weights (an overload). Find

the time t, measured from the start of the motion, in which each
load traverses a distance $S = 1$ m, and the speed v of the loads
after traversing this distance.

90. Using the data of the previous problem find the pressure p
exerted by the extra load on the original load during the motion.

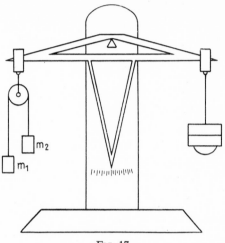

FIG. 17

91. The device described in Problem 86 is mounted on a balance
with a braked pulley* (Fig. 17). (1) In which direction is the equilibrium of the balance broken if the brake is taken off the pulley?
(2) How does the balance reach equilibrium when the masses m_1,
m_2 are in motion?

92. Find the accelerations a_1, a_2 of the masses M_1, M_2 and the
string tension T in the system illustrated in Fig. 18. Neglect the
weight of the pulleys and string.

93. Find the acceleration of the mass m_1 in the system illustrated
in Fig. 19. Find the string tensions T_1 and T_2. Neglect friction and
the weights of the pulleys and string.

94. Figure 20 illustrates a device for demonstrating the laws of
dynamics. Two extremely light pulleys a and c are mounted on the
beam of a balance, one at one end and one at the centre; attached
to the ends of a string passing round the pulleys are two equal

* Due to this, the masses m_1, m_2 do not move.

loads A and B of 250 g. The central pulley is mounted in such a way that the load on the string is below the support point of the beam. A scale with small weights is suspended at the other end of the beam.

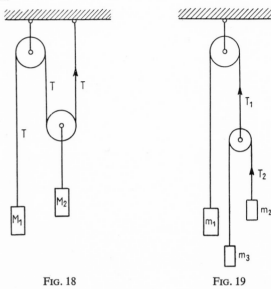

FIG. 18   FIG. 19

Let the balance be in equilibrium with the same loads A and B on the string. How must the load on the scale be varied so as to preserve the balance equilibrium with moving loads in the following

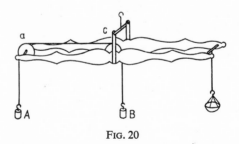

FIG. 20

cases: (1) an extra load of 25 g is placed on the load hanging from the end of the beam; (2) an extra load of 25 g is placed on the load under the mid-point of the beam?

95. The system illustrated in Fig. 20 (see the previous problem) is in equilibrium when an extra load of 50 g is placed on the central load and the pulleys are braked. (1) What must be done to re-establish equilibrium after the pulleys have been freed and the loads start to move? (2) Answer the same question, if the balance was first in equilibrium with the pulleys braked and an overload of 50 g placed on the load at the end.

96. A string of length l passes round a pulley whose axis is horizontal (see Fig. 15 for the arrangement of the pulley). Two monkeys hang from the ends of the rope at the same distance $l/2$ from the pulley. The monkeys start simultaneously to climb upwards; one climbs with a speed v relative to the rope, the other with a speed $2v$. How long does it take each monkey to reach the pulley? Neglect the weights of the rope and pulley; the monkeys both have the same weight.

97. The monkey moving with the greater speed (see the previous problem) has twice the weight of the other. Which monkey reaches the pulley first?

98. Two (solid) balls are falling in air. The balls are made of the same material, but the diameter of one is twice that of the other. What will be the ratio of the speeds of the balls in established (equilibrium) motion? Assume that the resistive force of the air is proportional to the cross-sectional area of a moving body and to the square of its velocity.

99. A steel ball of radius 0·05 mm falls into a wide vessel filled with glycerine. Find the speed v of the equilibrium motion of the ball. The coefficient of internal friction in glycerine is $\eta = 14$ g cm^{-1} sec^{-1}, the density of glycerine is $d_1 = 1·26$ g cm^{-3}, the density of steel $d_2 = 7·8$ g cm^{-3}.

Hint: To solve this problem, use has to be made of a well-known formula of hydrodynamics, expressing the resistive force exerted on the ball moving in a viscous fluid:

$$f = 6\pi r v \eta.$$

100. How will the speed of a body vary if it moves vertically upwards with initial velocity v_0 and it can be assumed that the air resistance is proportional to the speed of the body?

101. Two rain-drops start falling from a fixed cloud one after the other, τ sec apart. How will the distance between them vary in time?

Solve the problem in two cases: (1) on the assumption that there is no air resistance; (2) assuming that the air resistance is proportional to the speed of the drop.

102. A boat under sail develops a speed v_0. (1) How will the speed decrease in time in a calm sea after dropping the sail, if the resistance of the water can be regarded as proportional to the square of the speed? (2) How ought the boat to move? (3) What distance will it travel before coming to a complete stop?

103. Consider the questions put in the previous problem on the assumption that the resistance of the water is proportional to the first power of the boat's speed.

104. Let the resistance of the water to a boat be proportional to the speed of the boat (see also the conditions of the two previous problems). In this case, how will the speed of the boat after dropping the sail depend on the distance travelled?

105. A parachutist performs a delayed drop. Prior to opening the parachute he falls with a speed 60 m sec^{-1}, after opening, he lands with a speed 4 m sec^{-1}. Calculate what the maximum tension of the parachute chord would be if it opened instantaneously at the end of the delayed drop. The weight of the parachutist is 80 kg, whilst the air resistance to a moving parachute can be assumed proportional to the square of the speed (see also the next problem). Assume that the weight of the parachute and chord is small compared with the weight of the parachutist.

106. In the delayed drop considered in the previous problem, the parachute opens gradually instead of instantaneously. Throughout the period up to complete opening the cord tension T remains roughly constant and equal to 720 kg. Find the speed of descent v' at the instant when the parachute opens completely and the time τ taken for complete opening.

107. A string passes over a light pulley that rotates without friction. A weight of mass m_1 is attached to one end of the string. A ring of mass m_2 slides along the other end of the string with constant acceleration a_2 relative to the string (Fig. 21). Find the acceleration a_1 of the mass m_1 and the friction force R of the ring about the string. The weight of the string can be neglected.

108. The monkeys discussed in Problem 96 start to climb upwards with constant acceleration relative to the rope, one climbing with acceleration a, the other with acceleration $2a$. How long does it take each monkey to reach the pulley?

109. The various possibilities for the dependence of the motion of a heavy pendulum on the acceleration of its support point can be illustrated by the well-known experiments of Professor N.A.Lyubimov with a pendulum supported on a falling board. The axis of rotation of the pendulum is fixed near the top of the board, which falls vertically downwards, sliding without friction over guide wires (Fig. 22).

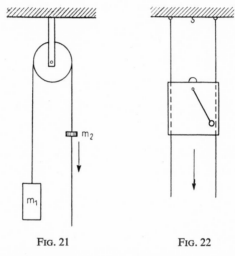

FIG. 21   FIG. 22

(1) How will the pendulum move relative to the board if it is inclined from the vertical whilst keeping the board fixed, and then both pendulums and board are freed simultaneously.

(2) How will the pendulum move relative to the board if it is first set into oscillation on the fixed board, and then the board is freed at the instant when the pendulum velocity is zero?

110. What will be the period of small oscillation of an ideal pendulum of length l, if it oscillates in a truck moving in a horizontal direction with acceleration a?

111. What will be the period of small oscillation of a pendulum in a lift, falling with constant acceleration a? What is the period when $a = g$? How does the pendulum behave if $a > g$?

112. What is the period of small oscillation T of a simple pendulum of length l, suspended in a trolley that rolls freely down a slope at an angle α to the horizontal?

113. A heavy body is suspended on a spring from the roof of a lift cage. How does the body move relative to the cage if the latter suddenly starts to fall freely under the action of gravity?

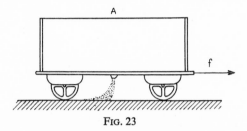

FIG. 23

114. Find expressions for the acceleration and speed of a trolley A under the action of a constant horizontal force f (Fig. 23) if it contains sand that pours out through the floor. The weight of sand pouring out in 1 sec is Δm; at time $t = 0$, the speed of the trolley was $v = 0$, and the weight of sand plus trolley was M.

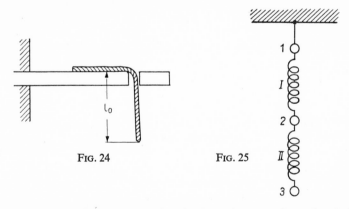

FIG. 24   FIG. 25

115. A rope lies on a board and one end passes through a hole drilled in the board (Fig. 24). Find the speed v with which the end slides away from the board, given that the total length of the rope is l and the length hanging initially from the hole is l_0. Find the length that has passes through the hole as a function of time. Neglect the friction between the rope and board.

116. Three equal balls 1, 2 and 3 are suspended on springs one below the other, in such a way that the distances between them are equal (Fig. 25). Thus the centre of gravity of the system is at the centre of the second ball. If the thread is cut that supports ball 1, the system starts falling, the acceleration of the centre of gravity of the system being $3mg/3m = g$ (by the familiar law: the acceleration of the centre of gravity of a system of bodies is equal to the sum of the external forces acting on the system divided by the total mass of the system). But spring I pulls ball 2 upwards more strongly that spring II pulls it downwards (the pull of spring I is $f_1 = 2mg$ at the initial instant, whilst the pull of spring II is $f_2 = mg$ at the initial instant), so that ball 2 starts falling with an acceleration less than g.

We thus seem to have arrived at a contradiction. (1) Explain the apparent contradiction; (2) find the accelerations of all the balls at the initial instant; (3) find the initial accelerations of the balls if we cut the spring supporting ball 3 instead of the thread.

117. A wedge of mass M lies on a horizontal plane (Fig. 26). A body of mass m is placed on the face of the wedge. All the contacting surfaces of the bodies are smooth. Find the horizontal acce-

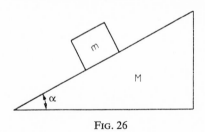

FIG. 26

lerations of both bodies and the forces N and R with which the body presses on the wedge and the wedge presses on the plane.

§ 3. STATICS

118. A man of weight P stands on a horizontal plane and supports by his weight with the aid of a fixed pulley a load of weight Q (Fig. 27). Find the force F with which the man presses on the plane.

119. A lamp of weight $P = 10$ kg is supported by a cable above the middle of a street of width $l = 10$ m. The permissible cable tension $p = 50$ kg. If the point at which the lamp is fixed to the cable must be at a height $h = 5$ m, at what height must the ends of the cable be held?

120. An analysis of the result of Problem 119 can lead to the following unexpected conclusion: a cable can be broken by an arbitrarily small force. For suppose the cable is stretched and clamped at it ends; we now only need to apply a small force perpendicular to the cable at its centre in order to produce as large a tension as desired. How is it that a cable cannot be broken by an arbitrary small force?

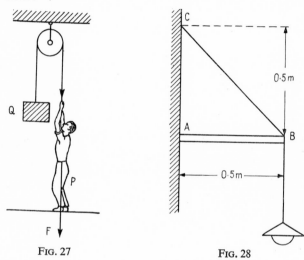

FIG. 27   FIG. 28

121. The suspension of a lamp is as illustrated in Fig. 28. The weight of the lamp is 5 kg. Find the forces acting on the girder AB and the wire CB (the dimensions are shown on the figure).

122. A rope is attached to a hook A and passes round a pulley C (Fig. 29). A load of 20 kg is fastened to the rope at the point D, which cannot move along the rope. What load Q must be attached to the end of the rope in order for the rope tension over the piece AD to be twice that in the remaining part, and the angle ADC to be 90°? Find the force F pulling out the pulley C.

123. A wedge is driven into a beam. What must be the coefficient of friction for the wedge not to slip out from the beam? The angle of the wedge at the vertex is 30°.

124. With what force f must a man pull on a rope in order to support the platform on which he stands (Fig. 30), if the weight of the man is $P_1 = 60$ kg and the weight of the platform $P_2 = 30$ kg? With what force F does the man press on the platform? What is the maximum weight of platform $(P_2)_{max}$ that the man can support?

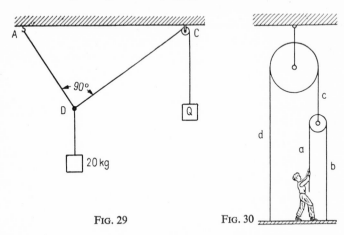

FIG. 29   FIG. 30

125. The construction and dimensions of a hoist are illustrated in Fig. 31. Find the pull F in the cable AB and the force T stretching

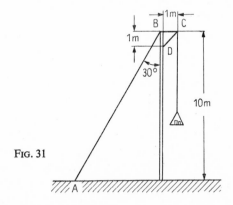

FIG. 31

the rod BC when the hoist lifts a 1 ton load. The points B, C and D are assumed to be hinged freely.

126. The length of a balance beam $2l = 30$ cm, the weight of the beam $p = 300$ g, the length of the pointer $D = 30$ cm. An overload

$p = 0.01$ g on one of the scales causes to the point to deviate $k = 0.3$ cm from the vertical. Find the distance d of the centre of gravity of the beam from the rib of the prism.

127. What minimum coefficient of friction k is required between the wall of a cube and a horizontal plane in order for it to tilt about its rib as the result of a horizontal force F being applied to the upper face? What must be the value of the applied force?

128. Find the distance d from the centre of gravity of a semi-circle of radius R from its diameter.

129. Find the distance d from the centre of gravity of a semicircular lamina of radius R from its diameter.

130. A uniform lamina is bounded by a semicircle of radius R and an isosceles triangle with base and height $2R$ (Fig. 32). Find the position x_c of the centre of mass C of the lamina.

131. Find the position of the centre of mass of a lamina in the form of a circular segment, the length of arc of which is 2α, and the radius R.

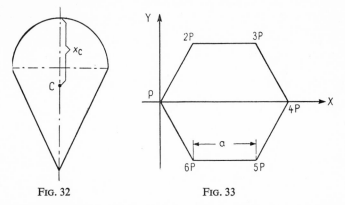

Fig. 32   Fig. 33

132. A semicircular plate is lifted at four points, two at the ends of the diameter and the other two on the circumference. What must be the distances of the last two points from the diameter in order for a quarter of the weight of the plate to be supported by each point?

133. Loads weighing P, $2P$, $3P$, $4P$, $5P$ and $6P$ are suspended from the six vertices of a horizontal regular hexagonal of side a (Fig. 33). Find the magnitude and point of application $M(x, y)$ of the resultant. The coordinate axes are as illustrated in the figure.

134. A uniform solid sphere of weight p, cut in half by a vertical plane and tied round its horizontal great circle with string, lies on a table. Find the string tension T.

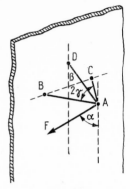

FIG. 34

135. A bracket, illustrated in perspective in Fig. 34, consists of three rods AB, AC and AD. The ends B, C, D of the rods are fixed to the wall by hinges, whilst the other ends are welded together at

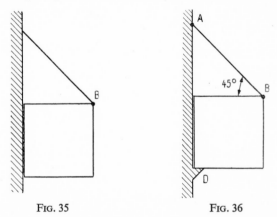

FIG. 35   FIG. 36

the point A. The rods AB, AC lie in a horizontal plane and form an angle 2γ. The vertical plane through the rod AD bisects the angle BAC. The rod AD forms an angle β with the wall. A force F acts at the point A, in a plane parallel to the wall and forming an angle α with the vertical. (1) Find the tension forces in the rods. (2) Find the conditions in which there is no tension in the rod AC.

136. Is it possible to support a box hanging from a rope against a vertical wall as illustrated in Fig. 35, when there is no friction?

137. A cube of weight 1 ton is supported by the rib D on a projection in a vertical wall and by a cable AB from the rib B to the wall (Fig. 36). The cable forms 45° with the wall. Find the force F exerted by the cube on the projection D.

138. Two identical beams rest on supports at their ends as shown in Fig. 37. There is no friction between the beams and the supports. A cylinder A is squeezed between the beams and held by friction forces, whilst the beams are joined from below by a rope attached

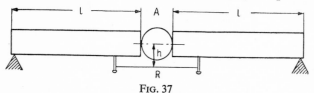

FIG. 37

to spikes driven into the beams. Find the tension T in the beams and the pressure F of the cylinder on the beams, given that the distance h between the axis of cylinder A and the rope is 20 cm. The length of each beam is $l = 1.5$ m, and the weight of each $P = 220$ kg, whilst the weight of the cylinder is $p = 20$ kg.

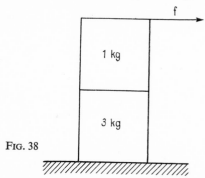

FIG. 38

139. Two cubes of edge length 10 cm are welded over their faces to form a prism; the weight of one cube is 1 kg, or the other 3 kg. The prism stands on a rough horizontal plane (Fig. 38). What horizontal force f must be applied to the upper face of the prism perpendicularly to its side in order to tilt it about the bottom rib? Does this force f depend on whether the lighter or heavier cube is at the top?

§ 4. WORK, POWER, ENERGY

140. A load weighing 10 kg is raised through 10 m by the action of a constant force of 20 kg. How much work is done? What is the potential energy of the raised load?

141. Find the work that must be done in order to tilt about its rib the prism described in Problem 139, for the cases mentioned there.

142. The coefficient of friction between a body and a plane inclined at 45° to the horizontal is 0·2. To what height will the body slide up the plane if it is given a velocity of 10 m sec^{-1} directed upwards along the plane? What will be the speed of the body when it returns to its initial starting point?

143. Show that, if a curve is drawn expressing the kinetic energy of a particle as a function of the path traversed, the force acting at each point in the direction of the path is measured by the slope of the energy curve with respect to the axis of abscissae.

144. It is required to pump out water into the roadway from a flooded cellar, the floor area of which is 50 m^2. The depth of water in the cellar is 1·5 m, whilst the distance from the level of the water to the road is 5 m. Find the work needed for pumping out the water.

145. Two litres of water are poured into the cylinder of a Barker's wheel; the height of this column is 60 cm. Find the energy U stored in the device.

146. A window blind weighing 1 kg and 2 m long rolls round a thin shaft at the top of the window. How much work is done in rolling it up? Neglect friction.

147. A mountain stream with flow section S m^2 forms a waterfall of height h m. The speed of the current in the stream is v m sec^{-1}. Find the power W of the stream, expressed in horse-power.

148. Find the mean useful power in a shot from a smooth-bored gun, given that the bullet of mass m leaves the bore with speed v_0, and the length of the bore is l (the pressure of the cartridge gases is assumed constant throughout the time the bullet is in the bore).

149. A plumb-line is held vertically in a truck travelling along a horizontal path with constant acceleration a, then is suddenly released. Find: (1) an expression for the potential energy U of the plumb-line when its angle of deviation from the vertical is α; (2) an expression for the work A done by the force deviating the plumb-line through the angle α; (3) the maximum value of the angle of deviation α_{max} in the conditions of the experiment. (4) Show that α_{max} is twice the angle to the vertical of the equilibrium direction of the plumb-line when the truck is in accelerated motion (see also Problem 82). (5) Describe the motion of the plumb-line after being freed from the vertical position.

150. A plumb-line is held vertical in a railway truck until the latter is travelling with constant speed. When the train brakes the plumb-line starts to swing, its maximum deviation from the vertical being 3°. What distance S does the train travel until it is at rest if its deceleration is assumed constant throughout and its speed at the initial instant of braking was 47 km hr^{-1}.

151. A meteorite falls from a very great distance to the earth's surface. At what speed would the meteorite strike the earth if the atmosphere did not brake its motion?

152. Do the results of the solution of the previous problem enable us to answer the question: what is the minimum speed required of a rocket fired from the earth's surface if it is to overcome the earth's gravitational force and reach interplanetary space?

153. A meteorite of mass $m = 1$ ton falls to earth from a very great distance. Find the kinetic energy T of the meteorite at a distance $h = 200$ km from the earth's surface.

154. What power W is expended by a horse in pulling a sledge up-hill with constant speed v? The weight of the sledge is p kg, the friction between the sledge and the hill is constant, the coefficient of friction is k. The angle of the slope of the hill is α.

155. Show that (for the conditions of Problem 102) the total work done by the friction forces between the boat and the water is equal to the initial kinetic energy of the boat.

156. Find the potential energy U of a compressed spring as a function of its deformation, on the assumption that the force of deformation is proportional to the third power of the size of the deformation, with coefficient of proportionality β.

157. A fly-wheel of radius R m does n revolutions per minute and transmits a power of P horse-power via a belt drive. Find the tension T (in kg) in the belt if it runs without slipping.

158. The power of a motor is determined by compressing its shaft A between two shaped blocks 1 and 2 (Fig. 39). The compression is supplied by a lever, perpendicular to the shaft, on which a load is suspended such that the lever retains its horizontal position when the motor is developing full power, turning in the direction

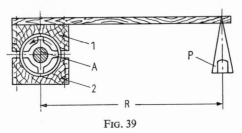

FIG. 39

indicated by the arrow. What is the power of the motor if a load P kg is situated at a distance R from the shaft axis when the motor is turning at n revolutions per minute?

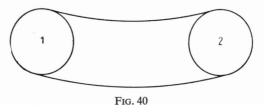

FIG. 40

159. Two pulleys at the same level are connected by a belt; the first is the drive pulley (see Fig. 40). In which case is the maximum power that can be transmitted by the belt for a given number of revolutions the greater; when the pulleys rotate clockwise or counter-clockwise?

§ 5. LAWS OF CONSERVATION OF MOMENTUM AND ENERGY

160. With what velocity v will a man start to move if he fires a shot horizontally whilst standing on very smooth ice? The weight of the man with rifle and bullet is 70 kg, whilst the weight of the bullet is 10 g and its initial velocity 700 m sec^{-1}.

161. Find the force exerted by a rifle on the shooter's shoulder on the assumption that a constant force acts towards the rifle and the shoulder is displaced $S = 1.5$ cm, whilst the bullet leaves the barrel instantaneously. The weight of the rifle is 5 kg, the weight of the bullet 10 g, and its exit speed is $v = 500$ msec^{-1}.

162. A shot is fired horizontally from a gun that slides freely on an inclined plane and has already traversed a path l. What must be the speed v of the shell in order for the gun to remain still after firing? Express the required velocity v in terms of the mass m of the shell, the mass M of the gun and the angle α of inclination of the plane to the horizontal. Assume that $m \ll M$.

163. A shell breaks into two equal parts at the top point of its trajectory at a height $h = 19.6$ m. One second after breaking, one part falls to earth at a point below that at which the breaking occurred. What is the distance S_2 from the firing point at which the second part of the shell falls, if the first part falls at a distance $S_1 = 1000$ m from the firing point? Neglect air resistance when solving this problem.

164. Three boats of the same weight P travel in line ahead (one after the other) with the same speed v. Loads of weight P_1 are thrown simultaneously from the middle boat to the front and rear boats with the same speed u relative to the boat. What are the speeds of the boats after the loads have been thrown across?

165. Two boats are travelling in opposite directions on a parallel course. When the boats are exactly opposite a sack weighing 50 kg is thrown from each boat over to the opposite one; as a result, the first boat stays still whilst the second travels at 8.5 msec^{-1} in its former direction. What were the speeds of the boats before exchanging the sacks, if the weights of the boats plus sack are 500 kg and 1 ton respectively.

166. A sphere of mass m_1 moving with speed v_1 is struck by a second sphere of mass m_2, which overtakes the first in the same direction with speed v_2. Assuming that the collision is completely inelastic, find the speeds of the spheres after the collisions and their kinetic energy.

167. Two spheres of mass m_1 and m_2 are travelling in opposite directions. An inelastic collision occurs between the spheres. The kinetic energy of one sphere is known to be 20 times that of the other. In what conditions will the spheres, after collision, travel in the direction of motion of the sphere with the lesser energy?

168. What must be the speed of travel of a shell of mass $m = 10$ kg if, when it strikes a vessel of mass $M = 100$ tons, the latter acquires a speed $v_1 = 0 \cdot 1$ m sec^{-1}? (Assume that the collision is inelastic.)

169. An ice-breaker striking an ice-flow of mass M gives it a speed of v m sec^{-1} as it pushes it away. Suppose that the pressure of the ice-breaker on the ice-flow increases uniformly in time as the ice-breaker approaches the ice-flow and also decreases uniformly when they move apart. Find the maximum force of the ice-flow on the side of the vessel in these conditions, if the collision occupies τ sec.

170. It is proposed in an invention to fill the tender of a train *en route* with coal by dropping it vertically from a suitably constructed bunker. What should be the tractive force applied to the tender if it is to be loaded with 10 tons of coal in 2 sec and proceeds uniformly for 10 min during this time? Neglect friction to the motion of the tender.

171. Find the work done by a locomotive during the loading of the tender with a mass Δm of coal (see the previous problem), and compare it with the kinetic energy received by the loading coal.

172. A piece of uniform cable hangs vertically, so that the lower end just reaches a horizontal table. Show that, if the upper end is released, the pressure of the cable on the table at any instant during its fall will be three times the weight of the part of the cable already lying on the table.

173. A ball falls vertically on to a wedge forming an angle of 45° with the horizontal. What will be the trajectory of the ball after striking the wedge? The surface of the wedge is smooth, the collision is complete elastic.

174. Find the momentum p received by a wall when a body of mass m collides elastically with it; the velocity v of the mass forms an angle α with the normal to the wall.

175. Find the change in kinetic energy ΔT and momentum Δp of a body, moving with velocity v, on elastic collision with a wall moving in the same direction uniformly with velocity $u < v$. What is the ratio u/v such that the body remains at rest on the wall?

176. A body of mass m_1 collides inelastically with a body of mass m_2. Find the fraction q of the kinetic energy lost if the body m_2 was at rest prior to the collision.

177. A lift descends with constant speed. What will be the tension in the cable from which the lift is suspended at the instant when the cable drum suddenly comes to a complete stop? How will the tension vary after this?

178. Calculate the maximum force T of the cable tension and its elongation (see the previous problem), if the coefficient of elasticity of the cable for the length at which the drum stoppage occurred is 1 ton cm^{-1}. The weight of the lift is 3 tons, its speed 10 m sec^{-1}.

179. A load of mass m hangs from a string of length l. Find the minimum height to which the load m must be raised in order for it to break the string when it falls, if the minimum static loading for breaking the string stretches it 1% prior to breaking. Assume that the force exerted by the string on the load is proportional to the string tension right up to breaking-point.

180. A ballistic pendulum is used for finding the speed of a shell. Its principle of operation consists in the shell whose speed is to be measured striking the bob of the pendulum (Fig. 41). Given the conditions of impact and the masses of the shell and pendulum, the

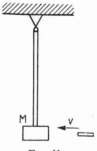

Fig. 41

speed v of the shell on collision can be determined from the angle of deviation α of the pendulum. Show how this is done for the following different cases: (1) the shell remains stuck in the bob after impact; (2) the shell rebounds after impact with speed v'; (3) the shell falls down, having lost its speed. The mass of the bob is M kg and the mass of the shell m kg; the pendulum can be regarded as ideal, its length being l.

181. Two spherical bobs, masses m_1, m_2, hang freely from strings of different lengths l_1, l_2, so that the bobs are in contact. The first bob is pulled through an angle α from its initial position in the plane of the strings and then released. A central collision of the spheres occurs. What are the angles a_1, α_2 of deviation from the vertical of the bobs after impact (the angles are assumed small and the impact elastic)?

182. A small body slides from a height h down a smooth plane inclined at 45° to the horizontal. How will the body move if, at the end of the plane, it encounters (1) a completely elastic horizontal plane, (2) an inelastic but smooth horizontal plane?

183. A box containing sand stands on an inclined plane; the coefficient of friction k of the box and plane is equal to the tangent of the angle α of inclination of the plane. A body falls vertically downwards into the box and remains there. Will the box move after the body has fallen into it?

184. The last truck gets uncoupled from a train travelling at constant speed and traverses a distance l before coming to rest. What will be the distance from the train to the wagon at the instant when the latter comes to rest, if the locomotive traction is constant, and the friction of each part of the train is independent of its speed and proportional to its weight?

185. A boat of mass M has a man of mass m standing on it and is at rest in a calm sea. The man starts to move along the boat with speed u relative to the boat. What will be the speed w of the man relative to the water? At what speed v will the boat now move relative to the water? Neglect the resistance of the water to the movement of the boat*.

186. Let the man traverse a distance l along the boat (see the previous problem). What will be the displacement S_1 of the boat and S_2 of the man relative to the water?

187. Let the man on the boat (see Problems 185 and 186) start to run along it with acceleration a relative to the boat. With what accelerations a_1 and a_2 respectively will the man and boat now move relative to the water? What is the force F exerted by the running man on the boat in a horizontal direction?

188. Two men of the same mass m are standing at opposite ends of the boat described in Problem 185 and throw a ball of

---

* The law of conversation of momentum must be applied in vector form when solving Problems 185–189.

mass Δm to one another. The speed of the ball relative to the water is u. Find (1) the speed of the boat v during the time the ball is in the air; (2) the displacement S_1 of the boat and S_2 of the ball relative to the water after each throwing of the ball across the boat, if the path length of the ball is l.

189. A particular form of the equation for the motion of a body of variable mass can be derived from a consideration of a simple case of the motion of a rocket. Let the rocket obtain its acceleration from the issue of a continuous gas jet, leaving the rocket at constant speed u relative to the rocket. The mass of gas issuing in unit time is μ, the mass of the rocket at a given instant is M. Find the equation of motion of the rocket.

190. The theory of rockets for interplanetary travel was developed by K. E. Tsiolkovskii. He obtained the relationship connecting the absolute magnitudes of the rocket velocity v and the issuing gas velocity u with the initial mass M_0 of the rocket and the mass of the rocket at a given instant M. Find this relation by using the results of the previous problem.

191. A reactive vessel of mass M is set into motion by a pump, which takes water from the river and ejects it behind the stern of the vessel. The velocity of the water jet relative to the vessel is constant and equal to u, whilst the mass of water ejected by the pump per second is also constant and equal to μ. (1) Find the absolute magnitude of the velocity v of the vessel as a function of time; (2) find the efficiency η of the system as a function of u and v. Find the maximum of the expression for the efficiency. Neglect friction forces in the pump and the resistance of the water to the movement of the vessel.

§ 6. DYNAMICS OF A POINT PARTICLE IN CIRCULAR MOTION

192. Find the force P with which a truck of mass m, moving with velocity v, presses on a bridge in each of the following cases: (1) a horizontal bridge; (2) a convex bridge (Fig. 42); (3) a concave bridge. (In cases (2) and (3) find P for the highest and lowest point of the bridge).

193. A ball of mass m slides from a height h down the smooth inner surface of a bowl in the form of a paraboloid of revolution with vertical z axis. The equation of the paraboloid is $z = k(x^2 + y^2)$. Find the acceleration a of the ball and the force F it exerts on the bottom of the bowl at its lowest point.

194. With what initial velocity v_0 must a bullet travel from a gun in a horizontal direction in order for it to go round the earth without dropping on to it? What will be the acceleration of the bullet in this case? (The radius of the earth $R \approx 6.4 \times 10^3$ km).

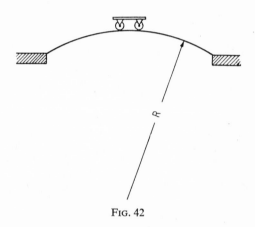

Fig. 42

195. Let a shot be fired from a gun at an angle to the horizontal, and let the initial velocity of the bullet be less than that obtained in the previous problem. What will the trajectory of the bullet be in this case and what will its acceleration be? (Neglect the air resistance to the motion of the bullet.)

196. A trolley of mass m slides without friction down a concave track of the shape illustrated in Fig. 43. (1) What is the minimum height H from which the trolley must start sliding in order for it not to leave the track throughout its length? (2) What forces act on the trolley at the highest point B of the loop? (3) What is the motion of the trolley if it slides from a height less than H? (When solving the problem, assume that the trolley wheels are of small size and small mass, and neglect their rotatory motion.)

197. What minimum coefficient of sliding friction k is required between the tyres of a car and the asphalt in order for the car to go round a bend of radius $E = 200$ m at a speed $v = 100$ km hr^{-1}?

198. When going round a bend radius R, a cyclist inclines inwards to the bend so that the angle between the plane of the cyclist and the earth is α. Find the velocity v of the cyclist.

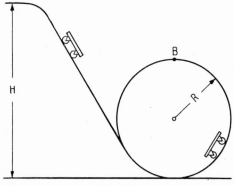

FIG. 43

199. A string of length l with a weight m at the end is fastened to a Γ-shaped support on the axis of a centrifugal device (Fig. 44). (1) What is the angle of inclination α of the string from the vertical

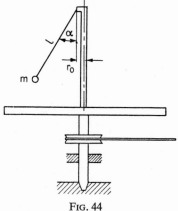

FIG. 44

if the centrifugal device rotates with angular velocity ω? (2) What is the tension T in the string in this case? (3) Will the string show a discontinuity of direction when the device rotates, if a small weight is fastened to the centre of the string).

Consider questions (1) and (2) for these two cases: (1) for small angles of inclination of the string from the vertical, corresponding to low angular velocity of rotation of the centrifugal device; (2) for arbitrary angular velocity of rotation of the device. The trigonometric equations obtained in the second case for the angle α should be solved graphically.

200. A ball of radius R hangs on a thread of length l and touches a vertical cylinder of radius r, mounted along the axis of a centrifugal device (Fig. 45). At what angular velocity of the device will the ball cease to apply pressure to the cylinder wall?

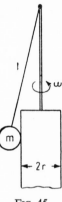

Fig. 45

201. A body is weighed on a spring balance in the wagon of a train travelling round a bend in the track which is banked in the usual way. The balance shows an n per cent increase in weight of the body as compared with the reading obtained in the train when travelling at constant speed in a straight line. The balance can revolve freely about its support point and remains hanging at right angles to the floor of the wagon when rounding the bend. Find the radius of curvature R of the track, if the train is travelling at speed v.

202. When an aeroplane loops the loop, the force acting on the wing differs from the loading in horizontal flight.

Suppose an aeroplane, weighing 3/4 ton, loops a loop of radius $R = 125$ m, travelling at a speed 120 km hr^{-1}. Find the maximum loading on the wings. Find the position along the trajectory at which the loading is a maximum.

203. An aeroplane loops a loop of radius $R = 100$ m, travelling at $v = 280$ km hr^{-1}. What will be the pressure of the pilot's body, weighing 80 kg, on the pilot's seat at the highest and lowest points of the loop?

204. A pendulum is hanging in an aeroplane that loops the loop. Find the direction of the pendulum at the various points of the loop for different aircraft speeds v and a loop radius R.

205. A load of mass M can slide without friction along a rod a, mounted perpendicularly to the axis of rotation of a centrifugal device (Fig. 46). The axis of the device is vertical, and a string is threaded through it, from which is suspended a load of mass m; the string passes round a pulley c and its other end is attached to the load M. Find the position of the mass M on the rod a when the centrifugal device rotates with angular velocity ω.

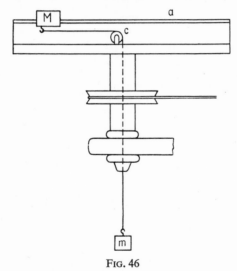

FIG. 46

206. In the previous problem, the axis of the centrifugal device intersects the horizontal rod a. What will the answer be if they do not intersect?

207. What will be the position of the mass M on the rod, if the entire device described in Problem 205 (Fig. 46) is given a rotation of angular velocity ω, after which the device is disconnected from the drive of the centrifugal machine? Will the mass M have a stable position on the rod? The moment of inertia of the device can be neglected by comparison with the moment of inertia of the mass M. Take no account of friction in the bearings of the device.

208. What may be the position of the mass M in the previous problem if the moment of inertia J_0 of the device itself cannot be neglected?

209. The rod of a device similar to that described in Problem 205 carries two masses m_1 and m_2 to one side of the axis of rotation; these masses are tied together by a string of length L. The mass m_1 nearer to the axis is joined by a thread of length R to the axis of rotation. Find the tensions in the strings, given the angular velocity ω of the device.

210. In the device described in Problem 205, a spring, instead of the mass m, is attached to the string, the other end of the spring being rigidly fixed. Given an angular velocity ω of the device, what must be the properties of the spring for the mass M, to be in equilibrium at any distance from the axis of rotation? There is no tension in the spring when the mass M is on the axis of rotation.

211. In the device described in Problem 205, a mass $M = 100$ g is connected by a spring with the axis. What is the coefficient of elasticity of the spring k, given that it is extended 50 per cent of its original length when the angular velocity of rotation $\omega = 120$ r. p. m.?

212. In the device illustrated in Fig. 47, the triangle CDE rotates about a vertical axis AB with angular velocity ω. A small coupling K can slide without friction along the rod CD which forms the hypotenuse of the triangle. What will be the position of K?

213. The board of a swing with people sitting on it weighs P kg. What is the maximum tension T in the ropes, if the swing is pulled $45°$ from its equilibrium position then allowed to swing?

214. On bends of a railway track the outer rail is slightly raised by comparison with the inner. Explain why this is done and calculate the necessary angle of slope of the rail bed.

215. A room that revolves about a vertical axis is occasionally arranged as an attraction. The floor of the room has a concave shape. During rotation, all the objects and people present stand on the floor as on a plane, normal to its surface and in a stable position. Find the shape of the floor if the angular velocity of the rotation is ω.

216. A small ball hangs like a bob from a string of length L, which is attached at the other end to the point O (Fig. 48). The bob is lifted to the right to the horizontal position 1 then released. At the point B, located at a distance $\frac{1}{2}L$ from the point O, there is a nail on which the string catches as it returns to the vertical position 2. Find: (1) the angle α to the vertical formed by the bob string at the instant when its tension becomes zero; (2) the velocity v of the ball at this point of its trajectory; (3) the geometrical curve of the bob trajectory after the string tension has become zero.

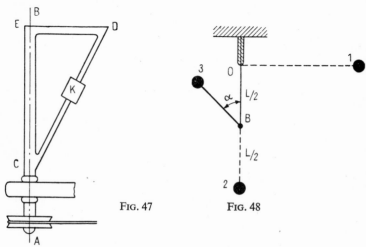

FIG. 47   FIG. 48

217. The daily rotation of the earth leads to a deviation of artillery shells and rifle bullets from the original direction of firing, specified in a horizontal plane with respect to the earth's orientation. Calculate the transverse displacement x of a bullet, fired in the meridian plane in a horizontal direction, after it has been travelling for one second. The shot is fired at the latitude of Moscow (55°45'), the initial speed of the bullet is 1000 m sec^{-1}. Find the direction in which the bullet deviates if the rifle barrel was directed southwards at the instant of firing. Neglect the air resistance to the bullet. Solve the problem in a coordinate system fixed in the earth.

218. A locomotive weighing 100 ton is travelling from south to north at a speed $v = 72$ km hr^{-1} at a latitude 60° N, along a railway laid along the meridian. Find the magnitude and direction of the force that the locomotive exerts on the rails in a direction perpendicular to the path of the train

219. A train weighing 100 ton is travelling from west to east at a speed $v = 72 \, \text{km hr}^{-1}$ at latitude 60° N, along a railway laid along the geographical parallel of the point in question. Find the magnitude and direction of the vertical and horizontal components of the Coriolis force acting on the train.

220. The daily rotation of the earth causes a deviation of falling bodies to the east. Find the distance x to which a body, falling freely from a height $h = 100 \, \text{m}$ at the equator, deviates on the earth's surface from the radius of the earth that passes through the initial position of the body. Solve the problem in a coordinate system fixed in the earth.

221. Solve the previous problem by using a coordinate system not fixed in the rotating earth, but in the solar system instead. It is recommended that two methods be used: (1) direct application of the laws of dynamics to the falling body and (2) application to the body of the law of conservation of angular momentum. What change is there in the result if the experiment is carried out at a point at the geographical latitude φ?

222. The earth's rotation causes a deviation in the surface of the water in rivers from the horizontal position. Calculate the slope of the water surface in a river with respect to the horizontal at latitude φ: the river flows from north to south.

§ 7. DYNAMICS OF A ROTATING RIGID BODY. DYNAMICS OF A SYSTEM

223. Find the accelerations of the loads and the tension in the string in the device illustrated in Fig. 49, taking into account the moment of inertia J of the rotating pulley, on the assumption that there is no slip between string and pulley. Find the stress in the support A if the mass of the pulley is M.

224. A uniform cylinder of mass M and radius R (see Fig. 50) rotates without friction about a horizontal axis under the action of the weight of a load P, fixed to a fine string wound on to the cylinder. Find the angle φ through which the cylinder rotates as a function of time, if $\varphi = 0$ and $\dot{\varphi} = 0$ at $t = 0$.

225. Imagine that the load P (see the previous problem) consists of two equal parts, connected by a string. Find the tension T in this string.

226. Two fine strings, loaded by masses m_1 and m_2 (Fig. 51) are wound in opposite directions round a stepped cylindrical pulley.

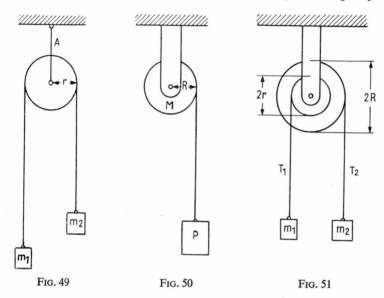

FIG. 49   FIG. 50   FIG. 51

Find the angular acceleration of the pulley and the tensions T_1 and T_2 in the strings, taking account of the moment of inertia J of the pulley.

227. A model of a capstan is clamped to one scale of a balance (Fig. 52). A string carrying a load of mass m is wound round the capstan, the moment of inertia of which is J. The scales are balanced whilst the capstan is braked and the string is not unwinding. What change must be made in the weights in the second scale of the balance in order to re-establish the equilibrium when the capstan rotates due to the load being allowed to fall downwards?

228. Under what conditions do the scales achieve a balance in the device described in the previous problem, when the load on the model capstan moves upwards due to the inertia of the untwisting flywheel?

229. The arrangement of a demonstration device (Maxwell disc) is illustrated in Fig. 53. A solid disc of radius R and weight P is rigidly fixed to a shaft of radius r. The shaft and disc are made

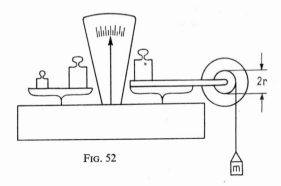

Fig. 52

from the same material, the weight of the parts of the axis projecting from the disc being p. The device is suspended from a support with the aid of strings of equal length attached to the shaft. The strings are wound up symmetrically on the shaft so as to raise the disc, then the latter is allowed to fall freely. Find the acceleration with which the disc drops.

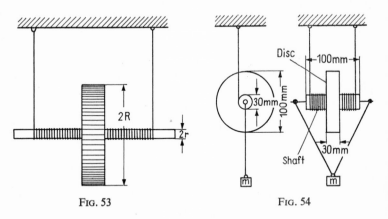

Fig. 53   Fig. 54

230. Find the acceleration a of the falling disc described in the previous problem if a mass $m = 314$ g is suspended by strings from a rod passing freely (without friction) through a hole inside the shaft (Fig. 54). The disc dimensions are indicated in the sketch; the disc and shaft are made of steel (specific weight 8 gcm^{-3}). The weight of the strings and axis are neglected.

231. What is the acceleration a with which a coil of mass M and moment of inertia J relative to the axis of symmetry falls, if it is suspended in the same way as the disc and shaft in Problem 229 (Fig. 55). Two further strings are wound on the coil, and from these a load of mass m is suspended. Find the tension in the strings.

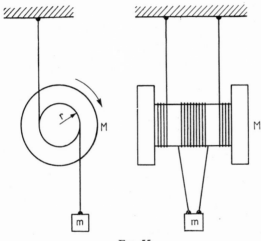

Fig. 55

232. Given two identical discs of devices as described in Problem 229, find the accelerations with which they fall if one is suspended from the other as shown in Fig. 56. The moment of inertia of the disc and shaft relative to the disc axis is J, the mass of the disc and shaft is m, the radius of the shaft on which the string is wound is r.

233. A solid uniform disc rolls without slip down an inclined plane forming an angle α with the horizontal. Find the linear acceleration a of the centre of the disc.

234. Find the acceleration a of the centre of a uniform sphere rolling without slip along an inclined plane, forming an angle α with the horizontal. What is the friction force between the sphere and plane?

235. Find the kinetic energy T of a hoop of mass M that rolls without slip; the thickness of the hoop can be regarded as very small compared with its radius.

236. A solid uniform cylinder of mass 300 g rolls without slip down an inclined plane forming $\alpha = 30°$ with the horizontal. Find the friction force between the cylinder and plane.

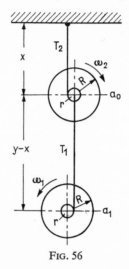

Fig. 56

237. What coefficient of friction k is required if a uniform cylinder rolls without slip down an inclined plane forming an angle α with the horizontal?

238. A solid cylinder and solid sphere of the same radii start to roll down an inclined plane simultaneously from the same level. (1) Which body will have the greater speed at a given level? (2) How much greater? (3) What will be the ratio of their speeds at a given instant?

239. Which of the shapes of the end of a shaft, illustrated in Fig. 57(a), (b) (with equal pressures on the bearing and equal speeds of rotation) is the more suitable from the point of view of less friction loss from rotation of the shaft in the bearing. (Friction about the side walls can be neglected.)

240. A string is attached to a truck standing on a horizontal plane and passes round a pulley fastened to the edge of a table; a load of mass $m_3 = 500$ g is attached to the end of the string. Find the acceleration a of the truck, given that the mass of the body of the truck is $m_1 = 1\cdot4$ kg, the mass of each wheel is $m_2 = 400$ g and the wheels are solid discs. The wheels roll without slip over the surface of the table, and there is no rolling friction.

241. A coil of rope lies on a horizontal table. What is the acceleration of the axis of the coil if it is pulled by the rope with a force F (Fig. 58)? How should the rope be pulled for the coil to move in the direction of the rope? (The coil moves without slipping over the surface of the table). Find the friction force between the coil and table.

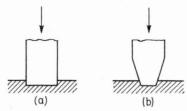

(a)   (b)

Fig. 57

242. A roller consists of a solid cylinder of radius R and mass M_1 (Fig. 59) and a frame of mass M_2. A mass M_3 is attached to the frame by a string. The entire system rests on an inclined plane form-

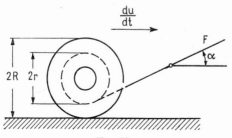

Fig. 58

ing an angle α with the horizontal. Find the acceleration a of the system, given that the coefficient of friction between the body M_3 and the plane is k. (The roller rolls without slip). How should the system be arranged – with the mass M_3 in front and the roller behind (as shown in the figure), or vice versa, in order for the string to be stretched during the motion?

243. A thin heavy uniform rod of length l hangs from a horizontal axis passing through one end. What initial angular velocity ω must the rod be given in order for it to rotate through $90°$?

244. Find the angular momentum N of the earth relative to its polar axis. Assume that the earth is a sphere of radius $R = 6000\,\text{km}$, of density $d = 5\cdot5\,\text{gcm}^{-3}$.

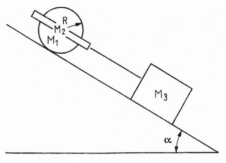

Fig. 59

245. What torque must be applied to the earth in order for its rotation to stop after 100,000,000 years (a year $= 366\cdot25$ "stellar" days).

246. A man of mass m stands on the edge of a freely rotating fairly large horizontal disc of radius R and moment of inertia J. The disc does n r.p.m. How does the speed of rotation of the disc vary if the man goes from the edge to the centre? How does the energy of the system vary in this case? Neglect the dimensions of the man compared with the radius of the disc.

247. A man of mass m stands on a uniform horizontal disc of mass M and radius R which is at rest. The disc can be rotated without friction about a vertical axis through its centre. The man starts to move at a certain instant. What is the angular velocity of the disc ω, when the man goes along a circle of radius r concentric with the disc, with velocity v relative to the disc?

248. An experimenter stands on a special stool and holds in his hands the vertical axis of a freely rotating wheel, having the moment of inertia J_1 relative to this axis AA (Fig. 60). The wheel rotates in a horizontal plane with angular velocity ω_1. The stool is so made that it can rotate freely about a vertical axis. The moment of inertia of the stool and experimenter about the vertical axis is J_2. The axis of the wheel and axis of the stool lie along a straight line. What is the change ΔE_k in the kinetic energy E_k of the entire system of stool and wheel, if the experimenter revolves the wheel axis through (1) 180°, (2) 90°?

249. A cylindrical rod of length $2l$ and weight p is attached at its mid-point to the end of a long wire, so that it is perpendicular to the wire. Two identical solid spheres are attached to the ends of the rod, so that the geometrical axis of the rod passes through their centres. Each sphere is of radius R and weight P. The twisting moment M of the wire is proportional to the angle α through which it is twisted, i.e. $M = k\alpha$. Express the angular acceleration $d\omega/dt$ of the system as a function of the given magnitudes and the angle of twist α, if the wire was first twisted and then the system left to itself.

250. With what part of a sabre should a stick be slashed in order not to feel the impact on the hand? Regard the sabre as a uniform lamina of length l.

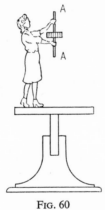

Fig. 60

251. A thin square uniform lamina of mass m_0 can rotate freely about a vertical axis (Fig. 61). A sphere of mass m, moving with speed v, strikes the plate normally at the point A, which is $2a/3$ from the axis. How do the plate and sphere move after impact. which occurs according to the law of elastic collision.

252. A uniform pine beam of mass M (density $0 \cdot 2$ gcm^{-3}), the dimensions of which are shown on the figure, can revolve freely about the axis AB (Fig. 62). The beam is struck horizontally at the point O by a moving body of mass $m = 10$ kg. What is the speed v of the body if the beam deviates through an angle $\varphi = 28°$ and the body falls at the point of collision?

253. A coupling piece weighing $p = 100$ g is fixed rigidly round the axis of a smooth horizontal rod that rotates about a vertical axis with constant angular velocity $\omega = 40\pi \, \mathrm{sec}^{-1}$.

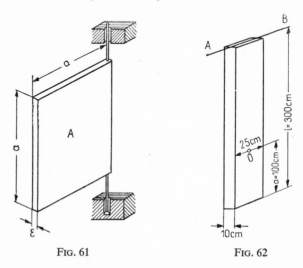

FIG. 61   FIG. 62

The coupling piece is freed at a certain instant, and slides without friction along the rod. Find the distance x of the coupling from the axis of rotation at any instant t. What moment M must be applied to the rod for it to continue its uniform rotation? At the initial instant the centre of gravity of the coupling is at a distance $a_0 = 2$ cm from the axis.

254. A solid cylinder of radius R, mass m, on which a string is wound, lies on two parallel horizontal beams. A force F, equal to half the weight of the cylinder, is applied to the end of the string that hangs down (Fig. 63). Find the horizontal acceleration of the cylinder and the minimum value of the coefficient of friction between the cylinder and beams such that rolling occurs without slip. The axis of the cylinder is perpendicular to the beams, its centre of gravity and the force F lie in the vertical plane through the midpoint between the beams.

255. A load of mass M is attached to the end of the string wound on a cylinder (as in Problem 254). The string passes round a pulley as shown in Fig. 64. Find the acceleration of the load M. Discuss the conditions in which the cylinder will slip when it rolls. The weight of the string and pulley, and the friction at the pulley axis, can be neglected. Assume that the motion of the cylinder is always plane-parallel.

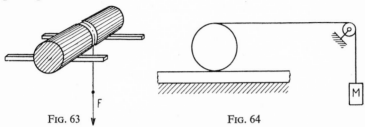

Fig. 63   Fig. 64

256. Two rollers, connected by a rod S, roll without slipping down a plane inclined at 30° to the horizontal (Fig. 65). The rollers have the same mass $m = 5$ kg and the same radii $R = 5$ cm, the moment of inertia of the first is $J_1 = 80$ kgcm², and of the second $J_2 = 40$ kgcm². The masses of the roller frames and rod can be neglected. Calculate the angular acceleration with which the rollers roll without slipping down the plane. Find the force transmitted by the rod, if the roller with the greater moment of inertia moves in front, and vice versa.

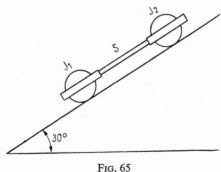

Fig. 65

257. A cylinder, radius R, mass m_3, can rotate freely about an axis, which is in turn fixed to a support of mass m_1. A string wound round the cylinder is attached to a body of mass m_2. Find the accelerations of masses m_1 and m_2 and of the cylinder in the following conditions. (1) A horizontal force F is applied to the mass m_2 (Fig. 66) and there are no friction forces. (2) The same conditions, except for the presence of friction between the plane and the bodies m_1 and m_2. Neglect friction at the cylinder axis. (3) A horizontal force F is applied to the point A and the mass m_2 removed; find the the accelerations of the mass m_1 and the cylinder. Assume that the motions of all the bodies are in a plane.

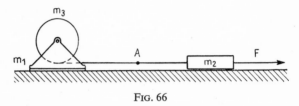

FIG. 66

258. A familiar method of distinguishing between a raw egg and a hard-boiled one is simply to try spinning it on a table. The hard-boiled egg spins for a long time, whilst the raw one will not spin. Explain the basis of this method.

259. The friction between an axle and an oiled bearing is primarily determined by the motion and internal friction of the liquid in the oil layer.

In N.P. Petrov's hydrodynamic theory of lubrication the following expression is given for the moment of the friction forces acting per unit length of the rotating axle:

$$M = 2\pi\mu a^3 \omega / \delta,$$

where μ is the viscosity of the lubricating liquid, a is the radius of the axle, ω is its angular velocity and δ is the thickness of the layer. Use this expression to find the law of rotation of a rotor, the shaft of which is secured in bearings; there are no other external moments acting on the rotor.

260. A solid cylinder of radius $R = 10$ cm and weight P is given a rotation about its axis with angular velocity $\omega = 600$ rev sec^{-1}. The rotating cylinder is placed on a horizontal plane and left to itself. Its starts to move along the plane, the coefficient of sliding friction between the cylinder and plane being 0·1. Determine the time T that elapses prior to the motion of the cylinder transforming to pure rolling without slip. The sliding friction is assumed independent of velocity, whilst rolling friction is absent. What will be the cylinder acceleration when $t > T$?

261. A solid cylinder whose axis is horizontal moves without rotation over a smooth horizontal plane in the direction perpendicular to its axis. At a certain instant it reaches a boundary, where the surface becomes rough and causes a constant (speed-independent) sliding friction, whilst rolling friction is absent. What is the motion of the cylinder after reaching the boundary? How is the kinetic energy of the translational motion of the cylinder distributed?

262. A body B (Fig. 67) is placed on top of a body A, situated on the horizontal surface of a table. What horizontal force F must be applied to the body A, in order for body B to slide from the surface of body A. The coefficient of friction between the body A and the table is μ_1, and between bodies A and B is μ_2. The masses of the bodies are m_A, m_B.

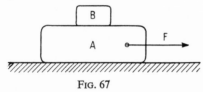

FIG. 67

263. Find the horizontal component of the acceleration a_2 of the body and the acceleration a_1 of the wedge (Problem 117, Fig. 26) under the following conditions. (1) Friction is present between the body and the wedge (coefficient of friction μ), but not between the wedge and the plane. (2) There is no friction between the body and the wedge, but between the wedge and the plane there is friction with coefficient μ. (3) Find the maximum coefficients of friction at which motion of the wedge and body will take place.

264. A rectangular prism stands on a rough board, lying on a horizontal table (Fig. 68). What is the minimum acceleration a_{min} with which the board must start to move along the table, for the prism to tilt over backwards (relative to the direction of motion of the board) about its lower back rib? Find the value N and coordinate x of the point of application of the vertical component of the force which the board exerts on the prism when the board moves with acceleration a.

Solve the problem in two coordinate systems, fixed to the board and to the table.

265. A car with a track width $2b$ and centre of mass at a height h above the ground travels round a horizontal bend of radius R. (1) Show that, when the speed of the car is $v > \sqrt{bRg/h}$, it turns over unless the wheels slide in a direction perpendicular to the car's motion. (2) Assuming that the speed of the car is sufficient for it to be capable of turning over, find the minimum coefficient of friction between the wheels and the road surface at which this can occur.

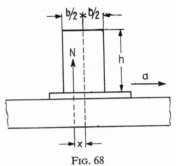

Fig. 68

266. A cylinder stands on a horizontal rotating disc. Find at what angular velocity ω the cylinder falls off the disc, if the distance between the axes of the disc and cylinder is R, and the coefficient of friction $\mu > D/h$, where D is the diameter of the cylinder and h is its height (Fig. 69).

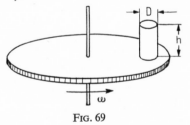

Fig. 69

267. A asks B to explain the following difficulty.

A — I understand how acceleration is communicated to a bicycle, but I do not understand how it is communicated to a locomotive. I picture the production of the force acting on the bicycle frame as follows: the action of the drive-chain on the rear wheel can be looked on as a force directed forwards and applied to the wheel at some point above the axis (Fig. 70). This force turns the wheel about an instantaneous axis through the point C, i.e. the point of contact of the tyre with the road, so that the wheel pushes the axis forwards and communicates motion to the entire machine. Is this right?

B — Yes. But you have not considered everything.

A — A locomotive can be considered in the same way, except that a locomotive has drive-gear instead of a chain, which makes a radical difference. For, when the point of application of the force from the drive-gear to the wheel is above the axle, the piston force pulls the wheels forwards, and here, as in the case of a cycle, the

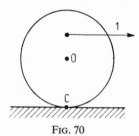

FIG. 70

wheel pushes the locomotive forwards. But after half a revolution the point of application of the force is below the axle, and the force is directed backwards. Arguing as above, we arrive at the conclusion: the wheel pushes the locomotive backwards. So how does the locomotive go forwards?

B — All your arguments about the forces acting on the wheel are correct, but ...

Discuss this problem.

268. Find the force f, acting from the rail on the wheel (see the answer to Problem 267), at the instants when the point at which the wheel is joined to the drive-gear (pin) is above (or below) the axle. Given: The piston force Q, the wheel radius R and the distance from the axle to the piston axis r.

269. Find the angular velocity of precession of an inclined top, precessing under the action of gravity. The top has moment of inertia J, angular velocity of rotation ω, distance from the support point to the centre of mass of the top l. In which direction does the top precess?

270. Calculate the moment M of the gyroscopic forces acting on the shaft from the propeller if an aeroplane flying at $u = 300 \text{ km hr}^{-1}$ makes a turn of radius $R = 100 \, m$. The moment of inertia of the propeller is $J = 7 \text{ kgm}^2$, and the propeller turns at $N = 1000 \text{ r. p. m.}$

271. A planet moves round the sun in an ellipse, the sun being at one of the foci. Show that the angular momentum of the planet relative to the sun is constant.

272. Use the results of the previous problem to show that the angular momentum of a planet about the sun can be written as $N = [r \times mv] = 2m\sigma = \text{const}$, where m is the mass of the planet, and σ is the areal velocity of the planet. The areal velocity of a planet is defined as the area described by the radius vector of the planet per unit time.

§ 8. Gravity

273. Find the acceleration g due to gravity on the earth's surface from the following data: the mean radius of the earth $R \approx 6400$ km; the mean density of the earth $d = 5.4 \text{ gcm}^{-3}$, the gravitational constant $\gamma = 6.7 \times 10^{-8} \text{ cm}^3 \text{g}^{-1} \text{sec}^{-2}$.

274. Find the acceleration g due to gravity at a height 20 km above the earth, taking the acceleration due to gravity at the earth's surface as $g = 981 \text{ cm sec}^{-2}$, and the radius of the earth $R \approx 6400$ km.

275. Find the acceleration due to gravity on the moon g_M if its radius is 1738 km, and the mean density is 0.6 times the density of the earth.

276. Calculate the acceleration a of a freely falling body on to the surface of the sun, if $R \approx 150 \times 10^6$ km is the radius of the earth's orbit, $r \approx 7 \times 10^5$ km is the radius of the sun and T is the time taken for the earth to revolve round the sun.

277. What acceleration a is communicated by the sun to bodies situated on the earth?

278. A pendulum that performs 3601.4 vibrations in an hour in Leningrad, performs 3600.0 vibrations in the same time in Moscow. By how much do the accelerations of freely falling bodies differ in these two cities?

279. How would the running of a pendulum clock differ on the moon, as compared with on the earth?

280. Jupiter takes 12 times as long as the earth to revolve round the sun. What is the distance in kilometres from Jupiter to the sun, if the distance of the earth from the sun is 150×10^6 km. Regard the orbits of the planets as circular.

281. Find the acceleration g_S due to gravity on the surface of the sun, given that the length of the terrestrial year is T, the distance from the earth to the sun is R ($\approx 8 \cdot 3$ light minutes) and the angle subtended by the diameter of the sun is α ($\approx 32'$).

282. Find the distance D of a planet from the sun, given that the mass of the sun is M, the period of revolution of the planet about the sun is T and the gravitational constant is γ.

283. The moon does a complete revolution about the earth in time $T = 27$ days and 7 hours. The radius of its orbits is 60 times the earth's radius. Find the acceleration due to gravity g on the earth. (The radius of the earth $R \approx 6400$ km.)

284. Find the potential energy of a body (point) of mass m at different distances R from the centre of the earth. Regard the potential energy at an infinitely great distance as zero.

285. Find the velocity v of an artificial earth satellite in a circular orbit of radius R. Express v in terms of R, the radius of the earth R_0 and the acceleration due to gravity g on the earth's surface.

286. Find the radius R of the orbit of a "stationary earth satellite". A satellite is said to be stationary if it moves in a circular orbit round the earth in such a way that one revolution takes 24 hours. A stationary satellite moving in the plane of the equator in the direction of rotation of the earth will remain fixed relative to it. Express R in terms of the earth's radius R_0, the angular velocity ω of the earth's rotation and the acceleration g due to gravity on its surface.

287. Two shots are fired with the same speed v_0 from a tower at a pole of the earth. The initial speed of the first short is directed so that the shot moves along the radius of the earth; the initial speed of the second is perpendicular to the radius of the earth, and it moves along an elliptic trajectory. Which shot reaches the greater distance from the earth? Find the ratio R_1/R_2 of the maximum possible distances from the earth's centre of the first and second shots respectively. The speed $v_0 > \sqrt{gR_0} = v_{\text{circ}}$, where v_{circ} is the speed of an earth satellite in a circular orbit (theoretical) with the radius of the earth R_0. Neglect air resistance to the shots and assume that only the gravitational field of the earth acts on the shots.

288. Two sputniks are fired into elliptic orbits from a point on the equator: the first in the direction of rotation of the earth, the second in the opposite direction. What are the maximum distances R_1, R_2 of the sputniks from the centre of the earth, given that their initial horizontal velocities relative to the earth have the same magnitude $v_0 = 10 \, \mathrm{km \, sec^{-1}}$? Find the distances in terms of the earth's radius R_0.

FIG. 71

289. Determine the second cosmic velocity, i.e. the velocity that must be communicated to a body for it to travel to an infinite distance from the earth. What must be the direction of the velocity relative to the vertical?

290. The maximum distance of the comet Gallea from the sun is $h = 35 \cdot 4$, its least distance $l = 0 \cdot 59$ (taking the distance of the earth from the sun as unit). The linear velocity of the comet is $v_1 = 0 \cdot 91 \, \mathrm{km \, sec^{-1}}$ at its point of maximum distance from the sun at the aphelion. What is the linear velocity v_2 of the comet when it is closest to the sun at the perihelion?

291. Prove that the force of gravity at any point A (Fig. 71), situated inside a cavity of a uniform spherical layer of gravitational matter, is zero. The mass is distributed uniformly between the two concentric spherical boundaries of the layer.

292. If we regard the earth as a sphere in which gravitational matter is distributed, the gravity force acting on a body (point) of mass m, located inside the earth, is $f = mgr/R_0$, where r is the distance of the point from the centre and R_0 is the earth's radius. Prove this, knowing that the gravity force outside a solid uniform sphere is proportional to its mass and inversely proportional to the square of the distance from the centre of the sphere.

293. Find the potential energy of a body (material point), situated in an imaginary vertical shaft through the centre of the earth. Regard the mass of the earth as distributed uniformly throughout the volume of the terrestrial sphere.

294. A body falls from the surface of the earth into an imaginary vertical shaft through the earth's centre. Find the velocity of the body when it is close to the centre of the earth. Neglect friction with the shaft walls and air resistance to the motion of the body.

295. Imagine a projectile of such dimensions that people and equipment can be accommodated inside it. Let the projectile travel in interplanetary space, with a certain acceleration due to the gravitational field existing in this region of space. What will be registered by a spring balance in the projectile, that has already been loaded on the earth? How can the mass of a body be measured during flight?

296. What will the spring balance of the previous problem register when a mass m is weighed, if the projectile gets into the atmosphere of a planet and receives, in addition to the acceleration from the gravitational field, an acceleration a cm sec^{-2} due to the resistance of the atmosphere to the motion of the projectile?

297. It is described in a book that, at a certain instant, the passengers in a rocket fired to the moon ceased to feel the presence of gravitational forces. When must this have occurred?

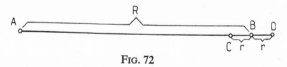

FIG. 72

298. A simple analysis of mechanical motions enables us to discover whether the rings of the planet Saturn are continuous formations or accumulations of small satellites. All we need to know for this is whether the inner or outer edge of the ring moves the faster. What are the laws on which this analysis can be based?

299. Four bodies A, B, C and D (Fig. 72), which can be regarded as material particles, rotating about a centre, always remain along the same straight line at a fixed distance from one another. Forces act between the bodies in accordance with Newton's law of universal gravitation. The masses C and D are equal and negligibly small by comparison with masses A and B, whilst the distance r is very small by comparison with R. What further forces must be exerted from body B on to C and D in order for the distances between all the bodies to remain unchanged?

300. The sun attracts a body on the earth with a certain force, which is directed at night in the same direction as the gravitational force of the earth on the body, whilst during the day it is in the opposite direction. Does this change of direction in the sun's gravitational force cause a change in the weight of a body during twenty-four hours?

301. By analysing the results of the previous problems, explain the occurrence of tides caused by the gravitational attraction of the moon. Calculate the tide-forming force, or the diminution in the apparent weight of a body, when it is close to the line joining the centres of the earth and moon.

302. Find the point on a straight line joining the earth and moon at which the intensity G of the resultant of the gravitational attractions of the earth and moon is zero. The mass of the earth is roughly 81 times that of the moon, and the mean distance between them is 384,000 km.

303. Neglecting the resistance of the atmosphere, find the minimum work that must be done in order to raise a mass of 1 kg from the surface of the earth to that of the moon. The radius of the earth is 6400 km and of the moon 1740 km; the acceleration due to gravity on the moon, caused by its own attraction, is $0.6\,g$, where $g = 9.8\,\mathrm{m\,sec^{-2}}$ is the acceleration due to gravity on the earth's surface. Neglect the influence of the sun and other planets.

§ 9. Elastic Deformations

304. The linear coefficient of thermal expansion of steel is $12 \times 10^{-6}\,\mathrm{deg^{-1}}$, Young's modulus $E = 2 \times 10^{12}$ in c.g.s. units. What pressure p must be applied to the flat ends of a steel cylinder for its length to remain unchanged when the temperature rises $100\,°C$?

305. Could a cable consisting of a thin copper wire in a lead sheath be used for telephone connection to a captive balloon at a height of 300 m. The limit of strength of lead is $2\,\mathrm{kgmm^{-2}}$, its density is $11.4\,\mathrm{gcm^{-3}}$.

306. When laying tramway rails they are made equal to one another at the joints. How great are the stresses p appearing in them for temperature variations from $t_2' = -25°C$ in winter to $t_2'' = +30°C$ in summer, if the laying is done at $t_1 = +15°C$? Young's modulus for iron $E = 2 \times 10^{-6}$ kgcm^{-2}, whilst the linear coefficient of heat expansion $\alpha = 1\cdot25 \times 10^{-5}$ deg^{-1}.

307. A steel cable that can support the weight of a lift cabin at rest has a diameter 9 mm. What must be the diameter of the cable if the lift cabin can have an acceleration of 8 g?

308. What is the variation in the volume of an elastic uniform rod of length l under the action of a force P, which either compresses or extends the rod lengthwise?

309. What uniformly distributed load Q can be supported by a granite block if it is in the form of a regular hexahedron of side $a = 10$ cm and the permissible stress on the compressed face is $p = 45$ kgcm^{-2}?

310. What is the extension of an iron rod hanging from one end due to the action of its own weight? What is the change in its volume?

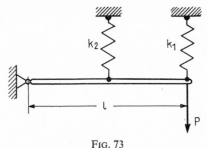

Fig. 73

311. A rod of length l is jointed to a wall at one end and is supported by two springs (Fig. 73); the spring at the end has a coefficient of rigidity k_1, and that at the middle rigidity k_2. Find the extensions of the springs and the stresses in them under the action of a load P applied at the end of the rod. The rod is assumed absolutely rigid and weightless, whilst the springs are not extended in the absence of an external load.

312. A load hangs from three ropes as shown in Fig. 74. The ropes are all made of the same material, and the two outer ones are identical. Find the ratio of tensions in the rope material, if the deformations on loading are extremely small.

313. A load of weight P hangs from three ropes as mentioned in the previous problem (Fig. 74). Find the stresses in the ropes if they all have the same cross-section and are made of the same material.

314. An absolutely rigid beam, to which a load P is attached, hangs from three ropes of the same length (Fig. 75). The ropes are made of the same material and have cross-sections S_1, S_2 and S_3. Find the stresses in the ropes P_1, P_2, P_3, if they are equidistant from one another and the load is attached to the mid-point between two of them. Find the conditions in which all three ropes are strained. The weight of the beam can be neglected.

315. A five-times safety factor for strength is chosen for rods. A steel rod with rectangular section (Fig. 76) has one end fixed into a wall. The ratio of height to width of the rod is $3:1$. (1) What load P is permissible at the end of the rod, if its length is 15 cm, and width 5 mm? (Breaking tension in the material is 100 kgmm^{-2}.) (2) Find the sag λ on bending at permissible loading. Young's modulus $E = 20,000$ kgmm^{-2}.

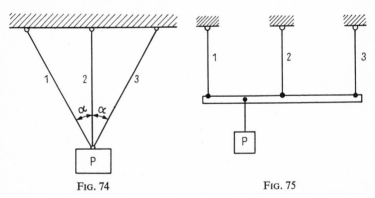

FIG. 74   FIG. 75

316. The ends of a beam are clamped to supports (Fig. 77), one support being movable. Find the sag λ of the beam under the action of a force P, applied to the mid-point of the beam. The length of the beam is l, the modulus of elasticity of the material is E and the moment of inertia of the cross-section is J. Regard the beam as weigthless and the bending as small.

317. Solve Problem 311 assuming that the rod is elastic (Fig. 73). Young's modulus of the rod material is E and the moment of inertia of the cross-section J.

318. The beam of a balance has a rectangular cross-section with sides $a = 8$ mm (horizontal) and $b = 10$ mm (vertical). The length of the beam is $l = 250$ mm. What is the maximum sag λ of the beam if the balance is designed for a maximum load $P = 500$ g, and Young's modulus for the material is 15,000 kgmm^{-2}.

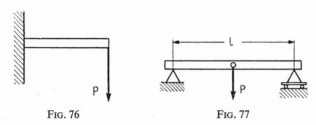

FIG. 76   FIG. 77

319. A wooden square-section beam of length $l = 4$ m and side $a = 40$ cm rests with its ends on two supports and carries a load $P = 2$ ton at its centre. What is the sag λ if Young's modulus for the type of wood in question is 1000 kgmm^{-2}?

320. The ends of a copper pipe, the outer and inner diameters of which are $D = 20$ mm and $d = 10$ mm, rest on two supports, the distance between which is $l = 400$ mm. The middle of the tube carries a load $P = 90$ kg. Young's modulus for copper is $E = 10^4$ kgmm^{-2}. Find the sag λ of the pipe midway between the supports.

321. A circular metal rod of radius $R = 10$ mm is clamped in a horizontal position by one end and a load $P = 1$ kg is suspended from the other end. The length of the rod is $l = 1$ m. The rod bends due to the load, the sag being $\lambda = 4$ mm. What is Young's modulus E for the material of the rod?

322. What change would there be in the expression for calculating Young's modulus E_1 in the previous problem if the rod were clamped at both ends and the load placed at the middle.

323. A rod of circular section is mounted vertically and clamped at its upper end. A horizontal pulley radius $R = 50$ mm is fixed to the lower end. The axis of the rod passes through the centre of the pulley. Two strings pass tangentially from the ends of a diameter of the pulley, and are acted on by equal forces $P = 5$ kg, twisting the pulley in the same direction. Through what angle φ does the rod twist? The modulus of displacement of the rod material is $N = 8000$ kgmm^{-2}, the rod radius is $r = 5$ mm, its length is $l = 1$ m.

324. A disc of mass m kg is mounted eccentrically on a thin vertical shaft; the distance between the disc centre and the shaft axis is d mm. A horizontal force applied to the shaft at the position where the disc is fixed is known to produce a deformation proportional to the force. The coefficient of proportionality is k kgsec^{-2}. Find the bending ξ of the shaft at an angular frequency of rotation of the shaft ω sec^{-1}. Neglect the mass of the shaft compared with the mass of the disc.

325. It is shown by experiment that the velocity v of propagation of the momentum of a transverse deformation along a stretched uniform string depends on the tension F and the mass ϱ per unit length of the string. Use dimensional analysis to find an expression for the velocity v as a function of these two parameters.

326. The frame of a sensitive galvonometer, rotating between the poles of a magnet, is suspended on a fine platinum wire or thin bronze strip. Find the maximum permissible weight of the frame if the limit of strength of platinum ≈ 30 kgmm^{-2}, and a wire of diameter 4μ is used for the suspension.

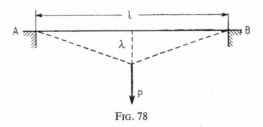

Fig. 78

327. Experiment shows that the velocity v of propagation of longitudinal deformations in a continuous medium depends on the modulus of elasticity E of the medium and on its density ϱ. Use dimensional analysis to find an expression for v as a function of these two parameters.

328. A wire stretches between two clamps A and B, a distance l apart (Fig. 78). A load weight P hangs from the mid-point of the wire and produces bending λ. Find λ as a function of P, given that Young's modulus is E, the diameter of the wire is d and $\lambda/l \ll 1$.

329. A steel wire, diameter $d = 1$ mm, bends round a drum, diameter $D = 2$ m. Find the extra tensions produced in the material of the wire if the modulus of elasticity of steel is $E = 2 \times 10^6 \, \text{kg cm}^{-2}$.

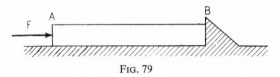

Fig. 79

330. A uniform beam AB of mass m, section S and length L is placed on a horizontal plane and rests against a projection at one end (Fig. 79). A constant force F acts on the other end of the beam, and is uniformly distributed over the section. In this case the length of the beam is well known to diminish by the amount $\Delta L = (1/E)(L/S)F$, where E is Young's modulus. The question is, what is the compression of the beam and how is it distributed if the beam does not rest against a support, whilst all the other conditions remain unchanged.

331. It follows from the previous problem that tension exists in a beam in accelerated motion. Will there be tension in a freely falling beam?

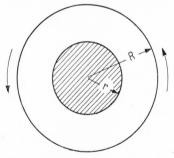

Fig. 80

332. A uniform disc of mass M and radius R rotates about its axis with angular acceleration β (Fig. 80). The forces accelerating the disc are uniformly distributed over its rim. Find the tangential force F acting per unit length of the circumference that forms an imaginary dividing line of radius r in the disc (shown shaded in the sketch).

333. A thin uniform elastic rod of length l, mass M, Young's modulus E, rotates uniformly with angular velocity ω about an axis perpendicular to the rod and passing through one end. Find the distribution of the stress T in the rod and its total elongation ΔL. When calculating the linear deformation and stress, assume that the cross-section is invariable and the elongation small.

§ 10. Vibrations

334. Draw the graphs of the displacement, velocity and acceleration in a simple harmonic oscillation as functions of time. Draw the graphs of the velocity and acceleration as functions of the displacement. Find the relationships between the amplitudes of the displacement, velocity and acceleration.

335. Find expressions for the potential, kinetic and total energies of a particle of mass m, performing harmonic oscillation in accordance with the law $A \cos \omega t$.

336. An areometer with a cylindrical tube (Fig. 81) of diameter D, floating in a liquid of density ϱ, receives a small vertical push. Find the period of vibration of the areometer, if its mass m is known. Neglect the motion of the liquid and its resistance to the motion of the areometer.

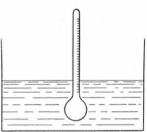

Fig. 81

337. Liquid is poured into a bent tube (Fig. 82), such that the two halves of the bend form angles α and β with the horizontal; the length of the liquid column is l. If the liquid is taken from the equilibrium position, its levels in the tube start to vibrate. Find the period of the vibration. Neglect capillary forces and the viscosity of the liquid.

338. A vertical cylinder of cross-section $S = 80 \text{ cm}^2$, is closed by a piston of mass $m = 1$ kg. The volume of cylinder below the piston is $v_0 = 5$ litres. At the initial instant the air pressure p_0 in the cylinder is equal to atmospheric. How does the piston move, if it is suddenly released? There is no friction between the piston and cylinder. Assume that the process of compression and expansion of the air is adiabatic ($\gamma = c_p/c_v = 1.4$).

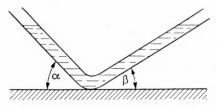

Fig. 82

339. What difference does it make in the previous problem if, instead of air, there is (1) hydrogen and (2) helium, in the cylinder. The remaining conditions are the same.

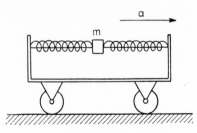

Fig. 83

340. Imagine a shaft bored along a diameter through the (spherical) earth. Find the law of motion of a body dropped into this shaft, taking into account the change in the acceleration due to gravity inside the earth. Neglect friction at the sides of the shaft and air resistance.

341. A block of mass $m = 1$ kg (Fig. 83) can slide without friction along a horizontal rod clamped into a trolley. Two springs are attached to the block, their common coefficient of stiffness being $k = 0.1 \text{ kgcm}^{-1}$. How will the load move relative to a coordinate system fixed in the trolley, in the following cases: (1) the trolley receives an acceleration that very slowly increases from zero to the value a; (2) at the instant $t = 0$ the trolley suddenly receives an acceleration $a = 0.98 \, \text{m sec}^{-2}$, which then remains constant. Assume that friction is very small.

342. Referring back to the previous problem, in the equilibrium state the centre of mass of the block is vertically above that of the trolley (Fig. 83). What sort of motion is produced, if the block is displaced $l = 6$ cm from the equilibrium position and attached by a string to the trolley, then the string cut. The total mass of the trolley (without block) is $M = 5$ kg, the mass of the springs can be neglected. Neglect friction forces.

343. Find the period of free small vibration of a load of mass m, attached at the mid-point of a thin string of length L (Fig. 84). The mass of the string can be neglected; the string tension is constant and equal to P.

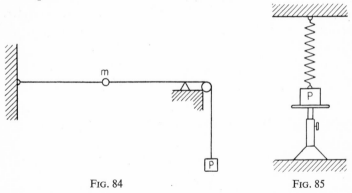

FIG. 84   FIG. 85

344. One end of a spring is clamped, and the other end is attached to a load of weight P, which lies on a support in such a way that the spring is not extended (Fig. 85). The support is removed without jolting. Find the motion of the load and the maximum tension in the spring. The coefficient of stiffness of the spring is k.

345. A load of weight $P = 1$ kg lies on a board. The board performs harmonic vibrations in a vertical direction with period $T = \frac{1}{2}$ sec and amplitude $a = 2$ cm. Find the pressure force F of the load on the board.

346. What is the required amplitude A of vibration of the board and load of the previous problem in order for the load to start jumping from the board?

347. A board performs harmonic vibrations in a horizontal direction with period $T = 5$ sec. A body lying on it starts to slide when the amplitude of vibration reaches the value $A = 0.6$ m. What is the coefficient of friction k between the body and the board?

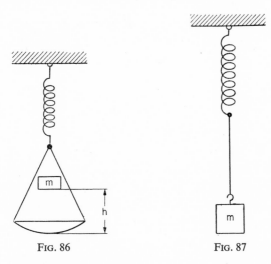

FIG. 86   FIG. 87

348. A load of mass m falls from a height h on to the scale of a balance, hanging from a spring (Fig. 86); the load does not bounce relative to the scale but stays on it. The scale starts to vibrate. The coefficient of stiffness of the spring is k. Find the amplitude A of the vibration (the mass of the scale plus spring can be neglected compared with the mass of the load).

349. A string, from which is suspended a load of mass m, is attached to a spring (Fig. 87). If the load is pulled down and then released, it starts to vibrate. To what distance x can the load be pulled down in order for the string to be stretched throughout the vibration? The coefficient of stiffness of the spring is $k = 0.05$ kg cm^{-1}, the weight of the body $P = 1$ kg.

350. A body is suspended from a spring and has a characteristic period of $\frac{1}{2}$ sec (Fig. 88). A sinusoidal force of amplitude $F = 100$ dyne acts vertically on the body, in addition to a certain friction force. Find the amplitude F_{fr} of the friction force and the coefficient of friction (the friction force is proportional to the speed of the motion), if the amplitude of vibration at resonance A_{res} is 5 cm.

351. A system performs forced vibrations under the action of an external force, which varies according to a harmonic law. Show that, at resonance, other things being equal, the work done by the external force per period is a maximum.

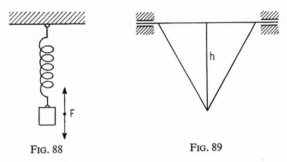

FIG. 88   FIG. 89

352. A uniform rod is suspended at both ends from two identical strings of length L. The strings are parallel in equilibrium. Find the period T of small vibrations, produced after a rotation of the beam about a vertical axis through its mid-point.

353. A fairly thin uniform plate is in the form of an equilateral triangle of height h. It can rotate about a horizontal axis, running along one side. Find the period of small vibration T of this physical pendulum (Fig. 89).

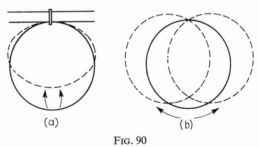

(a)   (b)

FIG. 90

354. A ring of thin wire performs small vibrations about a horizontal axis, like a pendulum (Fig. 90). In one case the axis lies in the plane of the ring (Fig. 90(a)), in the other it is perpendicular to the plane (Fig. 90(b)). Find the ratio of the periods T_1 and T_2 of small vibrations in these two cases.

355. A solid uniform disc, radius $r = 10$ cm, vibrates about an axis perpendicular to the plane of the disc and passing through a point of the rim. What length l would a simple pendulum require in order to have the same period of vibration as the disc?

356. A disc is made up of two halves, both of the same thickness but one of aluminium (specific weight $2 \cdot 5$ gcm^{-3}) and the other of

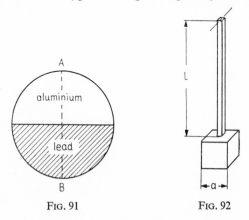

Fig. 91   Fig. 92

lead (specific weight 10 gcm^{-3}). In one case the axis of vibration, perpendicular to the plane of the disc, passes through the point A, in the other, through the point B (Fig. 91). What is the ratio of the periods of vibration about these axes?

357. A physical pendulum consists of a rod of square section suspended at one end, and a load clamped at the other end (Fig. 92). The load is a cube of side $a = 40$ mm; the rod is of length $l = 400$ mm and side of cross-section $b = 4$ mm; the load and rod are made of the same material. Find the approximate period of vibration T of the pendulum (the rod can be assumed thin in the calculation).

358. During oscillation with amplitude $\alpha_0 = 10°$ of the pendulum described in the previous problem, the load breaks off from the rod at the instant when the pendulum passes through its equilibrium position. What are the amplitude α_0' and period of vibration T of the rod after the load has broken off?

359. Answer the questions posed in the previous problem, when the load breaks off at the point of maximum deviation of the pendulum from its equilibrium position.

360. A thin uniform rod of length l swings about an axis through one end perpendicular to the rod. Is there a point on the rod such that, when a body of small dimensions but significant weight is clamped to it, the period of vibration of the rod is unchanged?

361. A small ring of mass m is mounted frictionally on a thin rod of length l. What force acts from the rod to the ring when the rod hangs from one end and vibrates as a pendulum with small amplitude α_0? The distance from the ring to the axis of the pendulum is d. The mass of the ring can be neglected when calculating the period of vibration.

362. A uniform plate in the form of an isosceles triangle is suspended from its vertices by three strings of the same length L. In equilibrium the plate is horizontal and the strings are vertical. Find the period of the torsional vibrations of the plate about a vertical axis (assume that each string deviates a small angle from the vertical).

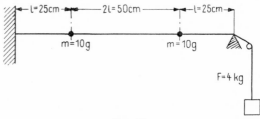

FIG. 93

363. Two masses, each 10 g, are fixed to a string with a constant tension of 4 kg, as shown in Fig. 93. What initial conditions must be specified for the loads in order for them to perform harmonic vibrations with the same period? Calculate the frequency of these vibrations (they are termed normal). Assume that the deviation during the vibrations is very small compared with l.

364. Prof. N. E. Zhukovskii proposed a device for a perfect (lossless) pendulum suspension as illustrated in Fig. 94. The collar A, seated on the shaft C, forms an integral part of the pendulum B. The shaft is mounted horizontally and revolves uniformly with angular velocity ω, and the pendulum performs vibrations in the plane perpendicular to the shaft.

Show that, if the angular velocity of the shaft is sufficiently large and the friction force of the collar on the shaft is independent of the sliding velocity, there is no loss of vibratory energy in the suspension. How great has the angular velocity of rotation of the shaft to be?

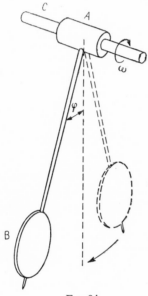

FIG. 94

365. What change is there in the nature of the vibration of the pendulum if the friction force of the collar on the shaft (Fig. 94) is dependent on the sliding velocity of the collar on the shaft, whilst the remaining conditions of the previous problem are unaltered. Consider two cases: (1) the friction force increases with the sliding velocity; (2) the friction force diminishes as the sliding velocity increases.

366. Find the position of equilibrium about which the pendulum described in the previous problem performs its vibrations. We are given that the friction force of the shaft on the collar is equal to μP, where μ is a constant, P is the pressure of the collar on the shaft; the distance from the axis of rotation to the centre of mass of the pendulum is equal to a and the shaft radius is R.

§ 11. Hydrostatics and Aerostatics

367. Two solid bodies of the same material hang from the ends of a lever with unequal arms and balance one another in the air. (1) Is the balance preserved if the bodies are immersed in vessels of water? (2) Does the balance change if the bodies are of different materials?

368. Of what material must weights be made in order to avoid the necessity, when weighing accurately, of making a correction for the loss of weight in air?

369. A hollow metallic sphere, the outer and inner diameters of which are d_1 and d_2, floats on the surface of a liquid. The density of the metal is δ_1, the density of the liquid δ_2. What weight p must be added inside the sphere in order for it to float below the level of the liquid? The compressibility of the sphere can be neglected.

370. What is the lifting force F of 1 m³ of helium filling a dirigible, if the density of helium relative to air is 0·137, and 1 m³ of air weighs 1·3 kg?

371. The balloon of a spherical aerostat has a volume 700 m³. The balloon is filled with hydrogen, 1 m³ of which weighs 90 g at a pressure of 1 atm. The weight of the basket, cover, all accessories and two passengers is 447 kg. (1) How much ballast $\Delta_1 Q$ must be added in order for the aerostat to establish itself close to the earth's surface at normal pressure? (2) How much ballast $\Delta_2 Q$ must then be thrown out in order to lift it a height of 2 km, if 1 m³ of air at this height weighs 1 kg? At the earth's surface 1 m³ air weighs 1·3 kg.

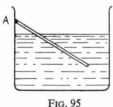

Fig. 95

372. At the bottom of a vessel containing liquid (or gas) a body is situated whose specific weight is much greater than the specific weight of the liquid (or gas). Is it possible to cause the body to lift upwards by increasing the pressure on the liquid (or gas)?

373. What is the pressure P of the air in a caisson dropped into water and intended for underwater work at the bottom of a river of depth h m, if the atmospheric pressure is H mm Hg? The density of mercury is d.

374. A thin rod is clamped at one end to the wall of a vessel, whilst the other end is submerged in water (Fig. 95). The rod can rotate freely about the horizontal axis of the hinge A, which is above the water level. Find the density δ of the rod material if, at equilibrium, $1/n$ of the rod is not submerged in the water. Neglect capillary forces.

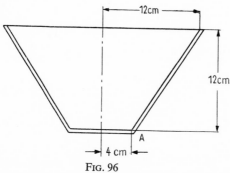

Fig. 96

375. Find the pressure force F of the water on the square wall of an aquarium (of side a). What is the height h from the bottom of the aquarium of the point of application of the resultant of the pressure on the wall?

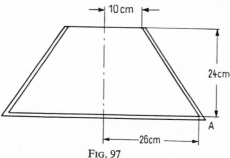

Fig. 97

376. A trough has the section shown in Fig. 96 and is filled to the top with water. Find the pressure P over 1 m length of the side wall and the moment of this force M about the bottom edge A.

377. A trough has the section shown in Fig. 97 and is filled with water. Answer the questions posed in the previous problem.

378. Find the resultant of the water pressure P in a river dam, trapezium-shaped as in Fig. 98, where $h = 5$ m, $d = 10$ m, $c = 15$ m.

379. A special shield is used to cover the water in a channel leading to a mill wheel. Find the moment of the forces acting on the cover relative to a horizontal axis lying in the plane of the cover at

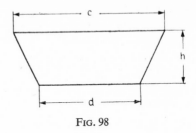

FIG. 98

a height 0·25 m above the level of the water, if the width of the channel is 1 m and the height of the level of the water trapped in the channel is 0·75 m.

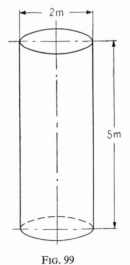

FIG. 99

380. Calculate the stress disrupting a vertical seam at a height $H = 1$ m in a cylindrical cistern filled to the top with water. The dimensions of the cistern are shown in Fig. 99.

381. A balloon of textile, which supports at bursting 850 kg per linear metre, is filled with gas.* When blown up the balloon is a sphere radius 10 m. What increase Δp of the pressure above atmospheric is permissible in the balloon?

382. At what height h is the density of the air in the earth's atmosphere halved; assume that the atmospheric temperature is fixed throughout its height. The pressure at the earth's surface is $p_0 = 10,330 \text{ kgm}^{-2}$ and the specific weight of air is $\gamma_0 = 1.293 \text{ kgm}^{-3}$.

383. A vessel containing water stands on a truck. The truck moves in a horizontal direction with acceleration $0.29\,g$. What is the angle α between the water surface and the horizontal?

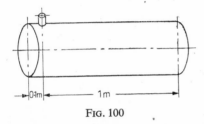

FIG. 100

384. A closed cylindrical vessel filled with water has a stopper at the top (Fig. 100). What is the acceleration a in a horizontal direction along the axis of the vessel that must be communicated to the vessel in order for the stopper to come out, if it can support a pressure of 0·05 atm, and the distance from the opening to one end of the vessel is 1 m, and from the other end 0·1 m.

385. What change would there be in the answer to the previous problem if, instead of being cylindrical, the vessel were a truncated cone, and the distances of the opening from the ends remained the same?

386. A goods train that includes an enclosed oil tanker moves with a speed v_0 then, as a result of braking, starts to decelerate uniformly and, after traversing a distance s, comes to a stop. Find the

* The elastic stress acting on any kind of envelope, casing, etc., is conveniently indicated by a force per unit length of the envelope cross section. The textile bursting strength mentioned in the problem implies that a strip of the textile 1 m wide can support without bursting a uniformly distributed force of 850 kg over its width.

oil pressure forces on the back and front walls of the tanker during
the period of braking. Assume that the tanker is a rectangular
parallelepiped of length l, width a and height h; the oil density is ϱ.

§ 12. Hydrodynamics and Aerodynamics

387. What is the speed v of flow of a liquid from the opening in
the wall of a vessel, if the height h of the level of the liquid above
the opening is 4·9 m? Neglect the viscosity of the liquid.

388. A tank is filled with water and oil (density 0·9 g cm^{-3}). What
is the initial speed v of flow of water from an opening in the bottom,
if the height of the water layer is $h_1 = 1$ m, and of the oil layer
$h_2 = 4$ m? (Neglect viscosity.)

389. Find the maximum pressure of a wind with speed 20 m sec^{-1}
on a horizontal wall if the wind blows perpendicular to the wall.
Express the pressure in millimetres of water column. The density
of air is 1·25 kg m^{-3}.

390. A cylindrical vessel that stands on a support has two openings 25 cm apart. The jets from the openings intersect. Find the
point of intersection, given that the water level is 25 cm above the
upper opening.

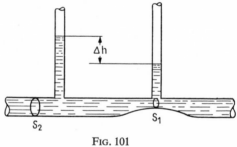

FIG. 101

391. Figure 101 illustrates a water-gauge: the water flows along
a horizontal tube of variable section. Find the outflow Q from the
difference Δh of the water levels in two manometer tubes, given the
sections of the main tube at the base of each manometer tube.

392. Figure 102 illustrates an arrangement whereby a locomotive
can fill up with water whilst travelling. A water-filled channel is
arranged along the track. A bent tube is attached to the locomotive

and drops into the channel in such a way that its mouth is directed forwards. Calculate the height h to which the water rises if the speed of the train is $v = 36 \, \text{km} \, \text{hr}^{-1}$. Neglect the viscosity of the water.

393. A sailor found a smallish hole in the hold of a vessel, through which water was pouring in; he tried to stop the hole with a plank

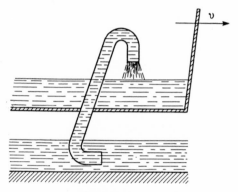

FIG. 102

but the stream of water pushed the blank away. He managed to bring the plank close against the hole with the aid of another sailor, and then found that he could hold the plank alone. Explain why the pressure on the plank is different in the two cases.

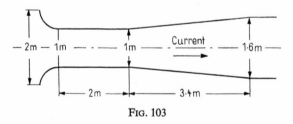

FIG. 103

394. An air current is produced in aerodynamic tunnels with the aid of a ventilator. The shape of a tunnel of circular section is shown in Fig. 103. It starts with a funnel-shaped opening, through which air is drawn from the surrounding atmosphere, then there is a cylindrical section, in which the model is located. The tunnel then widens and later becomes cylindrical again, the ventilator being mounted in this last section.

(1) Calculate the pressure Δp from the outside on the wall of the middle of the cylindrical section for a current speed $v = 100 \, \text{m sec}^{-1}$. (2) How is the result modified if the viscosity of the air is taken into account?

395. Figure 104 illustrates the arrangement of a pulverising device. Find the maximum height h to which it can pump liquid from

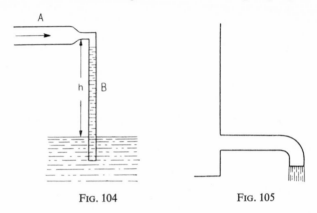

FIG. 104   FIG. 105

a reservoir if the pressure in front of the input into the tube A, where the velocity is very small, is p_0. Neglect viscosity.

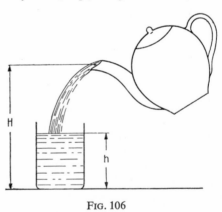

FIG. 106

396. Calculate the force F trying to pull the outlet pipe from a cistern of the cross-section of the jet is $S = 4 \, \text{cm}^2$ and the outflow of water is $Q = 24 \, \text{litre min}^{-1}$. The pipe has the shape shown in Fig. 105.

397. Find the dependence on time of the force F acting on the bottom, area S, of a cylindrical glass into which water is poured from a tea-pot, as illustrated in Fig. 106. A constant amount Q cm³ of water pours into the glass per second; ϱ is the density of the water.

398. A cylindrical vessel filled with water stands on a truck. The height of the water in the vessel is 1 m. On opposite sides of the vessel relative to the motion of the truck there are two taps, each

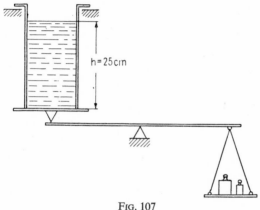

h = 25 cm

Fig. 107

with an opening area of 10 cm², one at a height $h_1 = 25$ cm above the bottom of the vessel, the other at a height $h_2 = 50$ cm. What horizontal force F must be applied to the truck in order for it to remain at rest when the taps are open?

399. A device for demonstrating the pressure of liquid on the bottom of a vessel (Fig. 107) includes a right cylinder containing water. The height of the water column in it is $h = 25$ cm. What change is there in the weight balancing the pressure on the bottom if a stream of water of cross-section $S = 1/4$ cm² flows through an opening in the bottom? The lowering of the water level in the cylinder can be neglected.

400. What change is there in the water pressure on the cover of Problem 379, if it is raised above the bottom of the channel so that a stream of water 5 cm high flows from below the cover, whilst the water level in front of the cover remains as before? Assume that the speed is constant over the height of the stream.

401. Find approximately the maximum power and most advantageous speed of rotation of a water wheel (as illustrated in Fig. 108), given that the head of water is $h = 5$ m, stream cross-section $S = 0.06$ m², wheel radius $R = 1.5$ m. The stream strikes the blades continuously and falls downwards after impact.

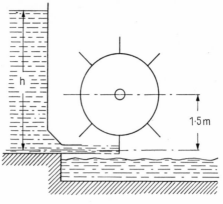

FIG. 108

402. The water flowing from the nozzle of a fire hose has a sufficient speed for the jet to reach a height of 20 m (neglecting air friction). What is the temperature rise of the water if the jet is directed into a closed fixed tank? Assume that the heat developed only goes into heating the water.

403. When discussing the design of a hydraulic ice-breaker (a machine for cutting ice by a jet of water at a pressure of about 60 atm), it was suggested that the cutting occurs due to the water heating up on impact with the ice and thus melting it. Discuss the correctness of this suggestion.

404. Find the shape of the free surface of a liquid, uniformly rotating with angular velocity ω about a vertical Z axis in a cylindrical vessel.

405. (1) Find the pressure distribution along a radius at the bottom of the vessel, given the conditions of the previous problem. (2) Find the pressure on the walls of the vessel close to the bottom if its angular velocity is 4 rev sec⁻¹. The height of the water column on the cylinder axis is 10 cm. The radius of the cylinder is also 10 cm.

406. A totally enclosed cylinder is filled with water and also contains: a cork, a small piece of lead and a body A whose density is equal to that of water. The cylinder rotates rapidly about its axis. How are the bodies disposed in the cylinder if the axis of rotation is vertical?

407. A cylinder filled with water rotates uniformly at 1 rev sec^{-1} about a vertical axis and carries the water along with it. A smooth horizontal rod, mounted along a diameter of the cylinder and submerged in the water, carries a cube of side 2 cm, made of a material with density $\varrho = 2$ gcm^{-3}. The cube is mounted so that it can slide on the rod and is supported by a small spring at a distance of 50 cm from the cylinder axis. Find the spring tension T.

408. In a rotating vessel the pressure on the bottom (see Problem 405) is greater at the wall than at the centre. Why does the water not flow from the wall to the centre when the vessel rotates?

409. Is it possible to measure the liquid pressure distribution in a rotating vessel by the following methods?

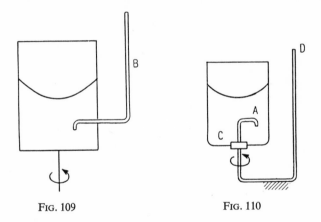

FIG. 109   FIG. 110

(1) A manometer tube B rotates along with the vessel and is filled with the same liquid as the vessel, as shown in Fig. 109. What is the liquid level in tube B when the system as a whole rotates, and what is the corresponding pressure? Capillary pressures in the tubes can be neglected.

(2) The manometer tube is in two parts, joined at the coupling C as shown in Fig. 110. The part AC is fixed rigidly relative to the

vessel, whilst the second part *CD* is rigid relative to the earth. The coupling *C* permits of a hermetic junction of the two parts and lies on the axis of the cylinder.

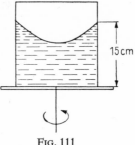

FIG. 111

(3) The manometer tube has the same form as shown in Fig. 110, but both parts of the tube are fixed to one another at the coupling *C*. Thus the part *AC* is also rigid relative to the earth. The part *AC* in the vessel is quite thin and does not affect the motion of the liquid. The rim of the opening *A* is horizontal.

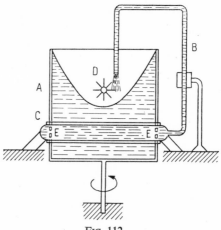

FIG. 112

410. The vessel illustrated in Fig. 109 contains oil above the water, and the height of the oil layer is 2 cm at its centre. What is the shape of the water surface now, when the vessel rotates about a vertical axis? What change is there in the height of the level in the tube. The oil density is 0·8 gcm^{-3}.

411. The water rotating in a vessel has the shape illustrated in Fig. 111. The height of the water at the vessel wall is $h = 15$ cm. Find the force F acting on a vertical strip of the wall 1 cm wide.

412. Someone suggested the following design for a perpetual motion machine. The vessel A (Fig. 112) is closely surrounded by a ring-shaped channel C with a tube B; the walls of the vessel have openings E, through which the liquid passes from the vessel into the channel C and tube B. The vessel A can rotate, whilst the channel C remains at rest. It is easily seen that, during rotation, a motion

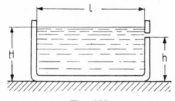

FIG. 113

of the liquid along the tube B is produced, provided the latter was filled by liquid in the first place. On uniform rotation of the vessel A the liquid passes round via the tube B, and the stream of liquid can be used to operate the water wheel D. The designer proposed that

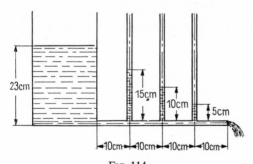

FIG. 114

part of the work of the water wheel be used, via a special transmission, to overcome the friction to the uniform rotation of the vessel (the transmission is not shown in Fig. 112). Why will this device not work?

413. The side wall of a vessel contains a hole, the lowest point of which is at a height h (Fig. 113). What is the horizontal acceleration a of the vessel such that liquid pouring into it does not come out through the hole, if liquid was poured into the vessel at rest (with the hole closed) to a height H?

414. Figure 114 illustrates a familiar experiment on the flow of a viscous fluid along a pipe, and shows the fall in pressure along the pipe. How can the fluid velocity be determined from the data indicated in the figure, if the fluid density is 1 gcm^{-3}.

415. An important formula for determining the lift of a wing is as follows: when an ideal fluid is in plane non-turbulent* flow round a body, the force acting upwards from the flow on an imaginary vertical cylinder of section dS is

$$\tfrac{1}{2}\varrho(v_1^2 - v_2^2)\,dS,$$

where v_1 is the velocity at the upper surface of the cylinder and v_2 the velocity at the lower; ϱ is the density of the fluid. Derive this formula.

§ 13. Acoustics

416. A bullet travels at 660 msec^{-1} at a distance of 5 m from a man. How far is the bullet from the man when he hears its whistle?

417. An echo sounder measures the depth of the sea from the reflection of sound from the sea-bed. What is the minimum accuracy required in determining the signal transmission and reflection times, if the device is designed for measuring depths exceeding 30 m to an accuracy of 5 per cent (the velocity of sound in water ≈ 1500 msec^{-1})?

418. A locomotive approaches an observer at 20 msec^{-1}. What is the fundamental tone of the hooter that he hears, if the driver hears a 300 c/s tone? What is the frequency variation of a harmonic of the hooter?

419. Two tuning-forks give 20 beats per 10 sec. The frequency of one fork is 256 c/s; what is the frequency of the other?

420. A tuning-fork that radiates sound of frequency v_0, is made to approach a distant wall at a speed u along the normal to the wall. A fixed sound receiver is located on the line along which the fork moves. Let: (1) the fork be situated between the wall and the

---

* In plane flow, every current tube lies in a plane parallel to some given plane. Non-turbulent flow is that in which the liquid flows smoothly round a body without forming vortices behind it.

receiver; (2) the receiver be situated between the fork and the wall. Will the receiver record acoustic beats if the speed u is much less than the velocity c of sound? What will be the frequency of these beats?

421. When measuring the speed of sound by the standing wave method (Fig. 115), the length of a half-wave of sound in air proved to be 6 cm. What is the speed v of sound in the rod, if the length of the rod is 60 cm and it is clamped at its mid-point?

Fig. 115

422. The length of a tube, closed at its ends, is 1·7 m. Find the proper frequencies N_k of the tube.

423. Find the frequencies N_k of resonance of a pipe, 1·7 m long and closed at one end.

424. Vibrations corresponding to the second harmonic are excited in a cylindrical open pipe. Illustrate graphically the distribution of particle displacement amplitudes along the pipe, and the distributions of velocity and pressure amplitudes. Indicate the places at which the potential and kinetic energies have maxima.

425. What is the length L of a string, if its frequency of vibration is increased one and a half times when it is made 10 cm shorter? The string tension remains unchanged.

426. Given two sources of vibration that yield systems of sinusoidal waves, find the motion of a particle situated at distances d_1, d_2 from the sources if they vibrate in the same phase and at the same frequency, and if the directions of the vibrations at the point in question are the same.

427. Find the adiabatic compressibility of water, if the speed of sound in water is roughly 1500 m sec^{-1}. (The coefficient of compressibility of a substance is equal to the relative decrease in its volume when the pressure increases by 1 atm.)

428. The speed of sound is 220 m sec^{-1} in liquid helium, which has a density of 0·15 g cm^{-3} at $T = 4.2$ °K.
Find the adiabatic compressibility β of liquid helium.

429. A rod of length $l = 1$ m is clamped at its ends. On rubbing, the rod produces a sound whose fundamental frequency is $\nu_0 = 700$ c/s. What is the speed of sound c in the rod? What overtones may be contained in the sound produced by the rod?

430. Two strings have the same length and tension. What is the ratio of their periods of proper vibration if the diameter of one string is twice that of the other? The strings are made of the same material.

431. What change is needed in the tension of a string if it is to produce a tone three times lower?

432. Explain why, for a given temperature, the speed of sound in air is independent of the barometric pressure.

433. Calculate the maximum acceleration and maximum speed of an air particle in an ultrasonic wave with frequency 50,000 c/s and particle displacement amplitude 0·1 micron.

434. A string produces a 400 c/s tone. At what point and in what way should the motion of the string be stopped in order for it to vibrate at (1) 800 c/s, (2) 1200 c/s? Is it possible to lower the frequency of vibration by stopping the string?

435. Show that, for any acoustic travelling wave, the relative pressure change dp/p at a given point is equal to the ratio of the particle to the sound velocity, multiplied by

$$\gamma = c_p/c_v,$$

where c_p and c_v are the specific heats of the medium at constant pressure and constant volume respectively.

436. A plane acoustic travelling wave can be represented by the equation

$$y = 0·05 \sin(1980t - 6x) \text{ cm},$$

where y is the particle displacement in the direction of wave propagation, t is the time in seconds, x is the distance in metres in the direction along which the wave is propagated. Find: (1) the frequency ν of the vibrations; (2) the wave propagation velocity c; (3) the wavelength λ; (4) the vibration amplitude of the velocity u

of each particle and (5) the pressure vibration amplitude Δp, if the pressure p and volume v are connected by the adiabat $pv^{1\cdot4} = \text{const.}$

437. Two sinusoidal plane waves are travelling in the same direction with propagation velocities v_1, v_2 and wavelengths λ_1, λ_2 respectively. Find the velocity u of displacement in space of the points where the vibrations corresponding to each wave have the same phase. Find the distance Δ between two similar points.

438. The concept of group velocity can be very easily visualised by analysing the following example. Let two groups, one of sportsmen, the other of sportswomen, move in series. In each group the members move one behind the other, with an interval d_1 between the women and d_2 between the men. The women's detachment travels at a speed v_1, the men's at v_2. Pairs of members pass a fixed observer at definite intervals of time. If the observer himself starts to move, he can diminish these intervals. At what speed u must the observer move for the sportsmen and women to pass him only in pairs?

439. The pressure amplitude of a sound wave is

$$\Delta p = 100 \text{ dyne cm}^{-2}$$

(loud sound).

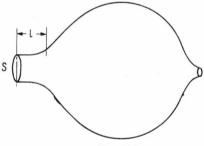

Fig. 116

Find the energy flux J, incident per 1 sec on a man's ear. The area S of the ear is taken as 4 cm² and the ear is perpendicular to the direction of wave propagation. The density of air is $\varrho = 1\cdot3 \times 10^{-3}$ g cm⁻³, the speed of sound is 334 m sec⁻¹.

440. A man with good hearing still finds a pressure vibration of 0·001 dyne cm⁻² at frequency 2000 c/s audible. Calculate the amplitude A of the air particle displacement in such a wave.

441. An acoustic resonator is usually a spherically-shaped cavity with a fairly narrow throat and a protuberance with a very small opening at the opposite end (Fig. 116). An acoustic wave leads to vibration of the air in the resonator throat. The mass of this air vibrates along the throat roughly like a solid body, whilst the air in the cavity plays the role of a spring in regard to this mass, since the speed of the air particles in the vibrations in the throat is large compared with their velocity in the cavity.

Find the period of the proper vibrations of the air in the resonator, assuming that we are given the cross-sectional area S of the throat, its length l, the volume v of the cavity and the speed c of sound in air. Use the analogy with Problem 338 on the vibrations of a piston closing a gas-filled cylinder.

442. What change is there in the frequency of vibration of the acoustic resonator if it is filled with hydrogen instead of air? (The density of hydrogen relative to air is 0·069.)

ANSWERS AND SOLUTIONS

§ 1. KINEMATICS

1. $|v| = \sqrt{5} \text{ m sec}^{-1}$; the velocity vector forms an angle $\alpha = 63°30'$ with the river bank from which the ship is departing.

2. The course of the boat must be at 39° to the straight line joining the landing-stages; $v_1 = 0.62 \text{ m sec}^{-1}$.

3. The tube must be inclined forwards from the vertical with respect to the path of the cart at an angle

$$\alpha = \arctan \frac{v_{\text{cart}}}{v_{\text{drop}}}.$$

4. $v = 9.3 \text{ m sec}^{-1}$; the wind direction is at 165° to the course of the vessel.

5. The distance between the aeroplanes increases by $\sqrt{v_1^2 + v_2^2} \times 1 \text{ hr} = 500 \text{ km}$ every hr; $S = 1500 \text{ km}$.

6. The gun has to be aimed ahead of the target ship so that the direction of the shell is at an angle

$$\varphi = \arccos \frac{v_1 + v_2}{v_0}$$

to the path of the ship from which it is fired.

7. *Solution:*

$$\frac{L}{t_1} = v_2 + v_1; \quad \frac{L}{t_2} = v_2 - v_1,$$

whence

$$v_1 = \frac{L}{2} \cdot \frac{t_2 - t_1}{t_1 t_2} = 7.5 \text{ km hr}^{-1},$$

and

$$v_2 = \frac{L}{2} \cdot \frac{t_2 + t_1}{t_1 t_2} = 17.5 \text{ km hr}^{-1}.$$

8. *Solution:* The fisherman overtakes the boat-hook at the same speed with which he left it (this is the speed of the boat relative to the water) and overtakes it an hour after dropping it in the water. During this hour the boat-hook has travelled 5 km. Hence the speed of the current in the river is 5 km hr^{-1}.

9. (1) $\varphi_1 = \arctan \dfrac{v_0}{v_1}$;   (2) $\varphi_2 = \arctan \dfrac{v_0}{v_1 + v_2}$;

(3) $v' = \sqrt{v_1^2 + v_0^2}$, $v'' = \sqrt{(v_1 + v_2)^2 + v_0^2}$.

10. 14·1 cm sec^{-1}.

11. $t_{max} = \dfrac{ld}{fv \sin^2 \alpha}$.

Hint: The train is at a distance $l/\sin \alpha$ from the photographer. The component of the speed of the train in the direction perpendicular to the line of sight (which alone causes blurring of the image) is $v \sin \alpha$. The speed of the image of the train on the photographic plate is

$$v_{im} = \frac{vf \sin^2 \alpha}{l} ; \quad t_{max} = \frac{d}{v_{im}}.$$

12. $S_1 = v_0 t_1 + \dfrac{at_1^2}{2}$;

$$S_2 = (v_0 + at_1) t_2 + \frac{at_2^2}{2},$$

and since $S_1 = S_2 = S$, we have

$$a = \frac{2S(t_1 - t_2)}{t_1 t_2(t_1 + t_2)} \approx -3 \text{ m sec}^{-2}$$

and

$$v_0 = \frac{S_1}{t_1} - \frac{at_1}{2} \approx 11 \cdot 5 \text{ m sec}^{-1}.$$

13. See Figs. 117 and 118 and the notes on them.

Figure 117(a): The dependence of the speed on time is described by $v = at.$*

* The relationships between the kinematic magnitudes and time, quoted here and in the solution of Problem 14, are found by graphical or analytical differentiation and integration.

Figure 117(b): The graph consists of alternating segments of horizontal ($v =$ const at $a = 0$) and sloping straight lines ($v = at$ with $a =$ const $\neq 0$).

Figure 117(c): The graph is composed of segments of horizontal lines and segments of parabolas, the equations of the latter being of the form

$$v = \frac{kt^2}{2}$$

(when $a = kt$), provided the points 1, 3, 5* are taken as the origins when drawing the parabolas.

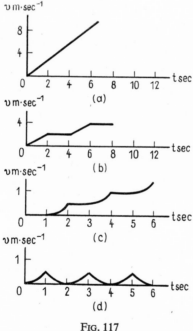

Fig. 117

Figure 117(d): The graph consists of segments of parabolas. Parabolas satisfying equations of the type $v = \frac{1}{2}kt^2$ are drawn from the points 0, 2, 4, 6. Over the pieces 1–2, 3–4, 5–6 of the time axis, the

* The k denotes a coefficient of proportionality, corresponding to the slope of the graph of a relative to the t axis; $[k] = $ cm sec^{-3}.

parabolas satisfy the equation

$$v = v_{max} - \frac{kt^2}{2}.$$

Figure 118(a): The equation of a parabola:

$$S = \frac{at^2}{2}$$

gives S as a function of t.

Figure 118(b): The graph consists of segments of parabolas (0–2, 4–6) $S = vt + \frac{1}{2}at^2$ and segments of sloping straight lines $S = vt$ over the pieces (2–4, 6–8, etc.) corresponding to $v = $ const. The dotted lines on the figure indicate the tangent to one of the pieces of parabola and the continuation of the straight segment of the graph corresponding to the piece 2–4 of the time axis.

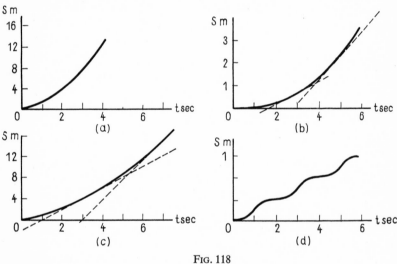

Fig. 118

Figure 118(c): The graph is composed of segments of parabolas satisfying an equation of the type $S = v_0t + at^3/6$, and straight segments with equations of the type $S = v_0t$.

Figure 118(d): The first piece of the graph has the equation $S_{0-1} = at^3/6$, the second $S_{1-2} = v_1t + at^3/6$, the third $S_{2-3} = at^3/6$. etc.

14. See Figs. 119(a) and (b) and the notes on them.

Figure 119(a): Over the piece 0–1 S is given as a function or t by $S_{0-1} = \frac{1}{2}at^2$, over 1–3, 3–4, 4–6 by

$$S_{1-3} = v_{max}t; \quad S_{3-4} = v_{max}t - \frac{at^2}{2}; \quad S_{4-6} = \text{const} \quad \text{etc.}$$

respectively.

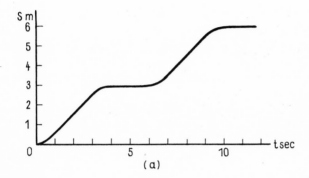

(a)

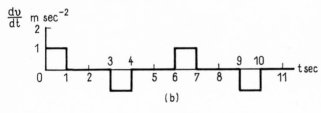

(b)

FIG. 119

Figure 119(b): Over the piece 0–1, $dv/dt = a = \text{const} > 0$. Over the pieces 1–3, 3–4, $a = 0$ and $a = \text{const} < 0$ respectively (see the note on the answer to Problem 13).

15. $v = \sqrt{2gh} \approx 6\cdot2 \text{ m sec}^{-1}$.

16. $S = 2v_0t$.

17. $v_0 = 82 \text{ m sec}^{-1}$.

18. At the highest point of the trajectory the normal acceleration will be a maximum, equal to the acceleration g due to gravity; at all other points of the trajectory it is equal to the projection of g on to the normal to the trajectory at the point concerned.

19. (1) $v_x = v_0 \cos \varphi$, $v_y = v_0 \sin \varphi - gt$,

$$v = \sqrt{v_0^2 + g^2 t^2 - 2v_0 \sin \varphi gt};$$

(2) $T = \dfrac{2v_0 \sin \varphi}{g}$;   (3) $\tan \alpha = \tan \varphi - \dfrac{gt}{v_0 \cos \varphi}$;

(4) $x = v_0 t \cos \varphi$, $y = v_0 t \sin \varphi - \dfrac{gt^2}{2}$;

(5) $y = x \tan \varphi - \dfrac{gx^2}{2v_0^2 \cos^2 \varphi}$;   (6) $H_{max} = \dfrac{v_0^2 \sin^2 \varphi}{2g}$;

(7) $L = \dfrac{v_0^2 \sin 2\varphi}{g}$, $\varphi^* = 45°$.

20. See Fig. 120.

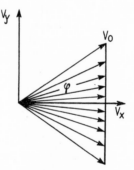

Fig. 120

21. $h_1 : h_2 : h_3 = 3 : 2 : 1$; $l_1 : l_2 : l_3 = \sqrt{3} : 2 : \sqrt{3}$.

22. $L \approx 40$ m; $\varphi \approx 38°40'$.

23. $|v|^2 = v_1^2 + v_0^2 - 2gtv_0 + g^2 t^2$; $\tan \alpha = \dfrac{v_0 - gt}{v_1}$,

where α is the angle between the vector v and the horizontal; the equation of the trajectory of the shell is

$$y = \frac{v_0}{v_1} x - \frac{g}{2v_1^2} x^2,$$

if the origin is at the point of space from which the shell was fired.

24. The equation of the trajectory is

$$y = \frac{b}{c} x;$$

$$v = 2t \sqrt{c^2 + b^2}; \quad a = 2 \sqrt{c^2 + b^2}.$$

25. $\tan \alpha = v \sqrt{\dfrac{2}{hg}}; \quad L = v \sqrt{\dfrac{2h}{g}}.$

26. $v = L \sqrt{\dfrac{g}{2\varDelta h}},$

where g is the acceleration due to gravity.

27. $v_0 = \sqrt{\dfrac{Lg \cos \alpha}{2 \cos \beta \sin (\beta - \alpha)}}.$

28. If α is the angle between the groove and the horizontal, and R the radius of the circle, a load will move along the groove with acceleration $g \sin \alpha$, and will traverse a path $l = 2R/\sin \alpha$ before reaching the circle. Thus the time taken to reach the circle is $\tau = \sqrt{4R/g}$, which is independent of the slope α of the groove.

31. $v = \sqrt{La}.$

Solution: Since it accelerates initially, then finally slows down, the average speed of the truck will be $\frac{1}{2}v$. It is clear from this that, the greater v, the shorter the time required for the motion. Thus the least time is required if the truck accelerates for half its path, and slows down during the other half.

32. If $v = v_0 t_0/t$ for $t \geqslant t_0$, we have

$$a = \frac{d}{dt} \left(\frac{v_0 t_0}{t} \right) = -\frac{v_0 t_0}{t^2} = -\frac{v^2}{v_0 t_0} \quad \text{for} \quad t > t_0.$$

33. (1) $S = v_0 t_0 \ln \dfrac{t}{t_0} \quad$ for $\quad t > t_0$

and

(2) $v = v_0 e^{-\frac{S}{v_0 t_0}} \quad$ for $\quad S > 0.$

These results are obtained as follows: $v = dS/dt = v_0 t_0/t$, consequently, $\displaystyle\int_0^S dS = v_0 t_0 \int_t^{t_0} dt/t$, or $S = v_0 t_0 \ln t/t_0 = v_0 t_0 \ln (v_0/v)$, whence follows the answer to the second question.

34. (1) $y = gx^2/2(v_a + v_s)^2$, the origin being at the firing-point; (2) $y = gx^2/2v_s^2$, the origin being at the aeroplane; (3) $y = -gx^2/2v_s^2$, the origin being at the shell. The x axis is always horizontal in the direction of the flight of the aeroplane, the y axis is vertically downwards.

35. The path of the boat will consist of the branches of two parabolas:

$$y = \sqrt{\frac{v\,dx}{n}} \quad \text{and} \quad y = d - \sqrt{\frac{d^2}{2} - \frac{vxd}{u}}; \quad x_0 = \frac{ud}{2v}$$

(see Fig. 121).

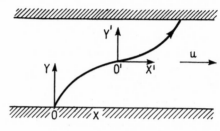

FIG. 121

Solution : The equations for the first parabola are found from the conditions: at $t = 0$,

$$x = 0 \quad \text{and} \quad y = 0\ (1),$$

and from the equations

$$v_y = v = \text{const}, \quad \text{or} \quad y = vt \tag{2}$$

and

$$v_x = dx/dt = ky = 2uy/d. \tag{3}$$

On integrating (3) and making use of (1) and (2), we get $x = uvt^2/d$. Elimination of time t gives the equation of the branch of the first parabola. On substituting $y = \frac{1}{2}d$ in it, we obtain the distance the boat goes down the river over the first half of its path. The equation of the branch of the second parabola is easily obtained as follows. We take a new origin O' of x', y' coordinates at the mid-point of the river, which the boat reaches at the end of the first half of its path. We now write down again the initial conditions of the motion: at $t = 0$, $x' = 0$ and $y' = 0$. Further, $y' = vt$, but $v_x = u - 2uy'/d$.

On solving these equations as in the first case, we find that $y' = \frac{1}{2}d$ $- \sqrt{(d^2/4) - (vx'd/u)}$. On returning to the previous coordinates, by means of the equations $y = y' + \frac{1}{2}d$, $x = x' + ud/4v$, we find the equation of the branch of the second parabola in the original coordinates. This branch of the second parabola is obviously a repetition in reverse of the branch of the first parabola.

36. The first half of the path of the boat is given by $y = \sqrt[3]{3vx/k}$, whilst the second half is the repetition in reverse of the first half, as in the previous problem. The boat travels $x_0 = kd^3/12v$ down the river.

37. At the point where the curvature is a maximum, i.e. near the point A.

38. $v = \dfrac{2\pi R}{T} = 3880$ km hr^{-1}.

$a = \dfrac{4\pi^2 R}{T^2} = 38\cdot1$ km hr^{-2}.

39. Straight lines parallel to the time axis.

40. $\omega = 0\cdot00093$ sec$^{-1} \approx 0\cdot001$ sec^{-1}.

41. $v \approx 7\cdot4$ km sec^{-1}.

42. $a_N \approx 0\cdot7\ g$.

43. $v = 1670 \cos \varphi$ km hr^{-1}, where φ is the geographical latitude of the point.

44. $v \approx 30$ km sec^{-1}.

45. $a_N = 0\cdot03 \cos \varphi$ m sec^{-2} and $a_R = 0\cdot03 \cos^2 \varphi$, where φ is the geographical latitude of the point; we have $a_N = 0\cdot017$ m sec^{-2} and $a_R \approx 0\cdot01$ m sec^{-2}, respectively, for Moscow.

46. $\alpha = \dfrac{\pi N^2}{n}$.

47. $n \approx 9$ rev sec^{-1}.

48. $a_N \approx 950$ m sec$^{-2} \approx 95\ g$.

49. $\alpha = 4$ rad sec^{-2}; $\varphi = 2t^2$ rad.

50. $a_N = 0.6 \, \text{m sec}^{-2}$; $a_{tot} = 0.67 \, \text{m sec}^{-2}$. The angle between $\boldsymbol{a}_{tot}$ and $\boldsymbol{R}$ is $153°$.

51. $v_x = v_0(1 + \cos \varphi) = 2v_0 \cos^2 \dfrac{\varphi}{2}$; $\quad v_y = -v_0 \sin \varphi$;

$$v_{tot} = 2v_0 \cos \frac{\varphi}{2}; \quad \alpha = -\arctan\left(\tan \frac{\varphi}{2}\right).$$

52. For both points of the wheel, $|\boldsymbol{v}_1| = |\boldsymbol{v}| \sqrt{2}$, where $\boldsymbol{v}$ is the velocity of rolling of the wheel; the velocity vector of the front point is inclined forwards and downwards at $45°$ to the horizontal diameter; the rear point velocity vector slopes upwards and forwards at the same angle. The acceleration vector of the front point is horizontal and in the opposite direction to the movement of the wheel. The acceleration vector of the rear point is horizontal and in the direction of motion of the wheel.

53. $x = R(\varphi - \sin \varphi) = R(\omega t - \sin \omega t)$,

$y = R(1 - \cos \varphi) = R(1 - \cos \omega t)$,

where $\varphi = \omega t$ and $\omega = v/R$ is the angular velocity of rotation of the wheel. The trajectory of a point on the periphery of the wheel is a simple cycloid, the parametric equations of which are given above (Fig. 122).

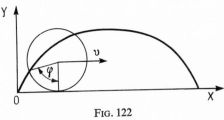

FIG. 122

54. $S = 8R$.

Solution: $v_{tot} = 2v_0 \cos \dfrac{\varphi}{2} = 2\omega R \cos \dfrac{\varphi}{2} = 2 \dfrac{d\varphi}{dt} R \cos \dfrac{\varphi}{2}$,

$$dS = v_{tot} dt = 2 \frac{d\varphi}{dt} R \cos \frac{\varphi}{2} \, dt = 2R \cos \frac{\varphi}{2} \, d\varphi.$$

Thus, to calculate the distance travelled by the point, the integration over time can be replaced by integration over the angle of rotation φ

of the wheel. The angle φ obviously varies between 0 and 2π between two successive contacts of the same point of the periphery with the road. We therefore have

$$S = 2 \times 2R \int_0^\pi \cos \frac{\varphi}{2}\, d\varphi = 8R.$$

55. $h_{\max} = R + \dfrac{v^2}{2g} + \dfrac{gR^2}{2v^2},$ \hfill (1)

$$[\cos \varphi]_{h_{\max}} = -\frac{Rg}{v^2},$$ \hfill (2)

where φ is the angular coordinate of the required point on the wheel periphery (see Fig. 6, Problem 53, p. 12).

Solution: We can write for the y coordinate of a point of the periphery:

$$y = R\left(1 - \cos \frac{v}{R} t\right)$$ \hfill (3)

(Fig. 6), whence

$$\dot{y} = v \sin \frac{v}{R} t.$$ \hfill (4)

The quantities y, $\dot{y}$ and h are connected by

$$h = y + \frac{\dot{y}^2}{2g}.$$ \hfill (5)

On substituting (3) and (4) in (5), we find (2) from the condition $dh/d\varphi = 0$. After this, (1) is obtained from (5) by making use of (2), (3) and (4).

56. $a_{\text{horiz}} = (v^2/R) \sin \varphi$; $a_{\text{vert}} = (v^2/R) \cos \varphi$. When the rotation is uniform, the total acceleration is always directed towards the centre of the wheel.

57. (1) $|a_N| = \dfrac{a_t^2 t^2}{R} = 2\alpha R \varphi$;

(2) $|a_{\text{tot}}| = \dfrac{a_t}{R} \sqrt{R^2 + a_t^2 t^4} = \alpha R \sqrt{1 + 4\varphi^2}$;

$$\tan \beta = -\frac{R}{a_t t^2} = -\frac{1}{2\varphi}.$$

58. The required axis of rotation must form an angle $\varphi = \arctan 0 \cdot 2$ with the vertical. The angular velocity about this axis must be $\omega_1 \sqrt{1 \cdot 04}$.

59. The cosines of the angles between the new axis of rotation and the three previous axes are given by

$$\cos \alpha = \frac{1}{\sqrt{14}}; \quad \cos \beta = \frac{2}{\sqrt{14}}; \quad \cos \gamma = \frac{3}{\sqrt{14}}.$$

The angular velocity of the rotation about the new axis is $\omega_1 \sqrt{14}$.

60. The required instantaneous axis of rotation will describe a circle of radius $r = \omega_2 R / (\omega_1 + \omega_2)$ about the axis of the first disc. The angular velocity about this instantaneous axis is $\omega = \omega_1 + \omega_2$.

61. When a car goes round a bend, its outer and inner wheels (relative to the centre of curvature of the bend) describe different circles, i.e. their paths are different, and the angular velocities of the wheels must be different if they are not to slip on the road. The differential fitted in the rear axle enables this condition to be fulfilled for the rear drive wheels. Since they are not rigidly connected with the engine, they can revolve independently of one another with different angular velocities.

62. $v_i = 9 \cdot 88 \text{ m sec}^{-1}$; $v_0 = 10 \cdot 12 \text{ m sec}^{-1}$.

63. If x is the horizontal displacement of the shadow of the stick on the screen, then $x = R \cos(\omega t \pm \varphi)$. Here φ is the angle between the plane of the screen and the vertical plane, drawn through the stick and the disc centre at the instant $t = 0$. x is measured from the point of the screen at which the light ray through the disc centre is incident. The oscillations of the shadow will obviously be symmetrical with respect to this point of the screen. The velocity v of the shadow and its acceleration a are given as functions of time by

$$v = \frac{dx}{dt} = -R\omega \sin(\omega t \pm \varphi) = R\omega \cos\left(\omega t \pm \varphi + \frac{\pi}{2}\right);$$

$$a = \frac{d^2 x}{dt^2} = -R\omega^2 \cos(\omega t \pm \varphi) = R\omega^2 \cos(\omega t \pm \varphi + \pi).$$

The graphs of x, v, a as functions of time are sine waves, displaced in phase relative to one another.

§ 2. Dynamics of Particle Motion Along a Straight Line and Elementary Systems

64. (1) $T = 0.5$ kg;   (2) $T = 1.5$ kg;   (3) $T = 0.9$ kg.

Hint: The balance readings can be found from the equation of motion of the body suspended from the balance:

$$ma = mg - T,$$

where m is the mass of the body, g is the acceleration due to gravity, T is the spring tension (which determines the balance reading) and a is the acceleration of the body of mass m.

65. $f = \dfrac{1}{6}$ kg; $f_1 = \dfrac{1}{3}$ kg.

66. $F_1 = -\dfrac{4}{5} F.$

67. $a = \dfrac{m}{m + M} g$; $T = \dfrac{Mm}{M + m} g.$

Solution: Since the string length is unchanged during the motion of the loads, both of those will move with an acceleration of the same magnitude a. The only force acting on the body M is the string tension T in the direction of the motion, whence

$$T = Ma. \tag{1}$$

Two forces act in the direction of motion (vertically) on the body of mass m: the gravitational force mg and the string tension T. Thus $mg - T = ma$; on taking equation (1) into account, the required quantities can be found.

68. (1) The upper half of the body exerts on the lower half a force whose vertical component is $\frac{1}{2}Mg$, and horizontal component $-\frac{1}{2}Ma$; (2) the left-hand half exerts on the right-hand half a horizontal force $-\frac{1}{2}Ma$, where a is the acceleration of the body.

69. (1) $a = \dfrac{M}{M + m_1 + m_2 + m_3} g$;

(2) $T_1 = (m_1 + m_2 + m_3)\, a,\; T_2 = (m_2 + m_3)\, a,\; T_3 = m_3 a.$

70. $a = g(\sin \alpha - k \cos \alpha)$.

71. $F \geqq 4$ kg.

72. The string tension is determined solely by the magnitude F of the force applied to the bodies; it is independent of the coefficient of friction between the bodies and the table, provided this coefficient is the same for each body.

73. $F > (m_1 + m_2) \, g$.

Hint: In order for the lower mass m_2 to rise from the table, the upper mass m_1 must bounce up so high that the spring is extended by an amount $x > m_2 g/k$ from its undeformed state, where k is the coefficient of elasticity of the spring. The mass m_1 bounces upwards from its static position (when the spring is deformed by its weight) through a distance which is equal to the distance that it falls from the static position as a result of the action of the external force F.

74. 1, 2 and 3 are the forces applied to the board. The forces 1 and 2 act away from the supports, whilst their reactions are applied downwards on the supports. The force 3 acts from the body to the board, whilst its reaction is applied to the body. (The reactions are indicated by dotted arrows, see Fig. 123.)

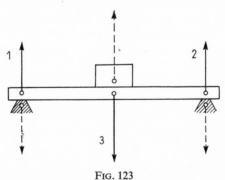

Fig. 123

75. The bending of the board decreases when the man squats down, and increases when he stands up.

76. Let A, B, C represent schematically the horse, sledge and earth respectively (Fig. 124). The sledge and earth exert forces F_2 and f on the horse, the forces exerted on the sledge are F_1 and f', and on the earth f_1 and f_1'.

By Newton's third law,

$$|F_2| = |F_1|; \quad |f| = |f_1|; \quad |f'| = |f_1'|.$$

Since the motion is uniform, we have by Newton's second law:

$$|f| = |F_2|; \quad |F_1| = |f'|; \quad |f_1| = |f_1'|.$$

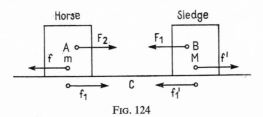

Fig. 124

77. By using the same arguments as in the previous problem, the following new relationships are obtained:

$$f - F_2 = ma; \quad F_1 - f' = Ma;$$

$f' = 0.2Mg$; since $|F_1| = |F_2|$ as before, we have

$$f = M(0.2g + a) + ma \approx 117 \text{ kg.}$$

78. (1) If all the wheels are driven, $k \geqslant a/g \approx 0.02$. In this case the minimum necessary coefficient of friction is independent of the weight of the car, since the friction force is proportional to the pressure of the wheels.

(2) If only the rear wheels are driven, $k \geqslant a/ng$, where n is the fraction of the total weight applied to the rear wheels; in the case in question, $n = 5/6$ and $k \geqslant 0.2/(5g/6) \approx 0.024$.

79. The acceleration of the board must be greater than 0.98 m sec^{-2}.

80. Greater than 2·25 kg.

Solution: The equation of motion of the board is $F - 0.5(m + M)g - f = Ma$, whilst the corresponding equation for the load is $f = ma$, where f is the friction force between the load and board, a is the acceleration. The maximum of f is $f = 0.25 \, mg$; consequently the maximum acceleration of the load is $0.25 \, g$ and the maximum force F, with which motion of the load and board as a whole will occur, must communicate to the board and load an acceleration $0.25 \, g$. We must have for this:

$$F = 0.25(M + m)g + 0.5(M + m)g = 2.25 \text{ kg.}$$

81. $\Delta M = 2 \left(M - \dfrac{P}{g} \right)$.

Hint: When the balloon is dropping, $Mg - P - R = 0$, when it is rising, $(M - \Delta M)g - P + R = 0$, where R is the air resistance.

82. (1) $\alpha = 0$; $T = mg$;

(2) $\alpha = \arctan \dfrac{a}{g}$, $T = m \sqrt{a^2 + g^2}$;

(3) $\alpha = -\varphi$, i.e. the string is normal to the inclined plane; $T = mg \cos \varphi$;

(4) $\tan \alpha = \dfrac{\dfrac{b}{g} \cos \varphi}{1 + \dfrac{b}{g} \sin \varphi}$; $T = m \sqrt{g^2 + b^2 + 2bg \sin \varphi}$;

(5) $\tan a = \dfrac{-\dfrac{b}{g} \cos \varphi}{1 - \dfrac{b}{g} \sin \varphi}$; $T = m \sqrt{g^2 + b^2 - 2bg \sin \varphi}$.

Here α is the angle between the string and the vertical; this angle is regarded as positive when the deviation of the string from the vertical is clockwise; the positive direction of the vertical is the same as the direction of the acceleration due to gravity.

83. (1) The acceleration is the same everywhere and equal to g. (2) The acceleration of the stone is greatest at the start of the motion, i.e. at the lowest point of its trajectory.

84. In the absence of air resistance, the acceleration is directed vertically downwards. In the presence of resistance the acceleration is inclined to the vertical, in a direction opposite to that of the motion of the shell.

85. When firing occurs vibrations are set up in the load A; when they are damped, the resultant force from the springs will be zero if air resistance is absent. If a force due to air resistance acts on the shell, the resultant force from the springs is $m(a - g)$, where both the shell acceleration a and the spring tension are assumed positive when they are directed downwards. This force is directed downwards when the shell is rising, and upwards when falling, i.e. it is opposed to the motion.

86. $a = \dfrac{m_1 - m_2}{m_1 + m_2} g; \quad T = 2\dfrac{m_1 m_2}{m_1 + m_2} g;$

$f = 2T = 4\dfrac{m_1 m_2}{m_1 + m_2} g.$

87. $a = \dfrac{m_1 \sin \alpha - m_2}{m_1 + m_2} g; \quad T = \dfrac{m_1 m_2}{m_1 + m_2}(1 + \sin \alpha)g.$

88. $\dfrac{m_1}{m_2} = \dfrac{n + 1}{n - 1}.$ This result is easily obtained from the answer to Problem 86, by putting $a = g/n$.

89. $t \approx 4 \cdot 5 \text{ sec}; \quad v \approx 44 \text{ cm sec}^{-1}.$

90. $p = \dfrac{2\Delta m g}{2 + \dfrac{\Delta m}{m}} = 4 \cdot 95 \text{ g}.$

91. (1) The balance inclines to the right, since, when the masses m_1, m_2 are in motion, the pressure force on the pulley axis is equal to twice the string tension $2T = 4m_1 m_2 g/(m_1 + m_2) < (m_1 + m_2)g$ (see the answer to Problem 86). (2) To maintain the equilibrium of the balance the load $(m_1 + m_2)g - 2T = (m_1 - m_2)^2 g/(m_1 + m_2)$ must be removed from the right-hand pan.

92. $a_1 = \dfrac{2M_1 - M_2}{2M_1 + \dfrac{M_2}{2}} \cdot g; \quad a_2 = -\dfrac{a_1}{2};$

$T = \dfrac{3M_1 M_2}{4M_1 + M_2} g.$

Hint: The condition connecting the accelerations a_1 and a_2 can be obtained thus: if x_1, x_2 denote the distances of masses M_1, M_2 from the horizontal plane, then $x_1 + 2x_2 = \text{const}.$

On differentiating this equation twice, we obtain the required condition $a_1 = -2a_2$.

93. $a_1 = \dfrac{m_1(m_2 + m_3) - 4m_2m_3}{m_1(m_2 + m_3) + 4m_2m_3} g;$

$T_1 = \dfrac{8m_1m_2m_3g}{4m_2m_3 + m_1(m_2 + m_3)};$

$T_2 = \dfrac{4m_1m_2m_3g}{4m_2m_3 + m_1(m_2 + m_3)}.$

Hint: If x_1, x_2, x_3 denote the distances of masses m_1, m_2, m_3 from the plane to which the pulley is attached, we can write: $x_2 + x_3 + 2x_1 = l_2 + 2l_1 + $ const, where l_1 and l_2 are the lengths of the strings. On differentiating this twice, we obtain the relationship between the accelerations of the three masses which is needed for solving the problem

$$a_2 + a_3 + 2a_1 = 0.$$

94. In both cases, the same weight has to be added to the scale pan:

$$\Delta p = \dfrac{1}{2 + \dfrac{\Delta m}{m}} g\Delta m \approx 12 \text{ g.}$$

95. (1) Add to the scale pan the weight

$$\Delta p = g\Delta m/(2 + \Delta m/m) \approx 22{\cdot}7 \text{ g.}$$

(2) Remove from the pan the weight

$$\Delta p = \dfrac{1 + \dfrac{\Delta m}{m}}{2 + \dfrac{\Delta m}{m}} g\Delta m = 27{\cdot}3 \text{ g.}$$

96. Both monkeys reach the pulley simultaneously, after time $\tau = l/3v$. Indeed, the rope tension is the same on both sides of the pulley. Hence the accelerations and velocities of the monkeys relative to the pulley are the same. Since they approach one another with a speed $3v$, they traverse the total path l in time $l/3v$.

97. The lighter monkey reaches the pulley sooner, inasmuch as its acceleration relative to the pulley is directed upwards, whereas the acceleration of the heavier monkey is downwards.

98. The speed of the larger ball is $\sqrt{2}$ times the speed of the smaller.

99. $v = \dfrac{2}{9} \dfrac{d_2 - d_1}{\eta} gr^2 = 0 \cdot 25$ cm sec^{-1}.

100. $v = \dfrac{mg}{r}\left[\left(v_0 \dfrac{r}{mg} + 1\right) e^{-\frac{r}{m}t} - 1\right]$,

where m is the mass of the body and r is the coefficient of resistance of the air.

Solution: The equation of motion has the form $mdv/dt = -mg - rv$. The result obtained above is found by integrating this equation with the initial condition $v = v_0$ at $t = 0$.

101. (1) $\Delta S = g\tau\left(t + \dfrac{\tau}{2}\right)$;

(2) $\Delta S = v_0\left[\tau + \dfrac{m}{r} e^{-\frac{r}{m}t}\left(1 - e^{-\frac{r}{m}\tau}\right)\right]$,

where v_0 is the steady-state velocity of a drop, r is the coefficient of resistance when the drops are falling in air. The time t is measured from the instant when the first drop starts to fall.

102. (1) The speed v of the boat will vary with time in accordance with

$$v = \frac{mv_0}{1 + rv_0 t},$$

where m is the mass of the boat and r is the coefficient of resistance of the water. (2) Given the assumption regarding the dependence of the resistance force on the speed, the boat must continue moving indefinitely and (3) the path traversed by it will also tend to infinity:

$$S = \frac{m}{r} \ln\left(1 + \frac{rv_0}{m} t\right).$$

However, this assumption concerning the resistance ceases to be valid when the speed of the boat is low; the resistance becomes proportional to the first power of the speed (see the next problem).

103. $v = v_0 \exp(-rt/m)$, and it is obvious that, with the given assumption, the boat will continue to move indefinitely. However, the condition $\lim_{t \to \infty} S = v_0 m/r$ will hold for the path S traversed by the boat after dropping the sail (see the result of the previous problem).

104. $v = v_0 - \dfrac{r}{m} S$, where the notation is the same as in the previous problem.

105. $T_{\max} = mgv_{\mathrm{fall}}^2/v_{\mathrm{landing}}^2 = 18{,}000$ kg.

Note: Neither the parachute cords, nor the parachutist on whom the cords would act with the same force, could sustain such a tension. In reality the parachute opens gradually, not instantaneously, and the tension is much less.

106. $v' = v_{\mathrm{landing}} \sqrt{T/mg} = 12 \ \mathrm{m\,sec^{-1}}$;

$$\tau = m(v_{\mathrm{fall}} - v')/(T - mg) = 0 \cdot 61 \ \mathrm{sec}.$$

107. $a_1 = \dfrac{m_1 g - m_2(g - a_2)}{m_1 + m_2}$; $R = \dfrac{m_1 m_2(2g - a_2)}{m_1 + m_2}$.

108. Both monkeys reach the pulley simultaneously, after a time $\tau = \sqrt{2l/3a}$. For, the force due to the rope tension is the same throughout its length, i.e. the monkeys have the same accelerations relative to the earth. They start to move simultaneously, approaching one another with acceleration $3a$; in order to reach the pulley, they both have to travel a distance l.

109. (1) The pendulum will fall with the board, without changing its relative position.

(2) The speed of the pendulum relative to the board ceases to vary as soon as the board starts to fall, and the pendulum starts to revolve about its point of suspension with this velocity.

110. $T = 2\pi \sqrt{\dfrac{l}{g'}}$, where $g' = \sqrt{g^2 + a^2}$.

111. $T = 2\pi \sqrt{\dfrac{l}{g - a}}$.

When $a = g$ the period becomes infinite, i.e. the pendulum does not oscillate. When $a > g$, the pendulum turns upside down and oscillates about its highest point with the period

$$T = 2\pi \sqrt{\frac{l}{a - g}}.$$

112. $T = 2\pi \sqrt{\dfrac{l}{g \cos \alpha}}.$

113. The body will perform oscillations on the spring. The amplitude of the oscillations will be equal to the spring extension due to the load in the fixed cage.

114. The acceleration of the trolley is $dv/dt = f/(M - \Delta mt)$. On integrating this equation and using the fact that $v = 0$ at $t = 0$, we get

$$v = \frac{f}{\Delta m} \ln \frac{M}{M - \Delta mt}.$$

115. $v = \sqrt{\dfrac{g}{l}(l^2 - l_0^2)}; \quad x = l_0 \cosh\left(\sqrt{\dfrac{g}{l}} t\right).$

Hint: The solution is obtained by integrating the equation $m\ddot{x} = mgx/l$, where m is the mass of the rope and x is the length of rope hanging down at a given instant from the table.
The initial condition is $v = 0$ at $l = l_0$.

116. In order for the distances between the balls to be the same, the springs must have different lengths in the unextended state (or have different elasticities), since the weight of two balls acts on spring I, and of only one ball on spring II. Hence:
(1) When the system as a whole falls freely, the centre of ball 2 will not be the centre of gravity of the system, and the acceleration of the mass of ball 2 is not the acceleration of the centre of gravity of the system, inasmuch as the distances between the balls vary due to the action of the springs. The centre of gravity of the system has constant acceleration g. At the initial instant the individual balls will have the following accelerations:

(2) $a_1 = 3g, \quad a_2 = a_3 = 0;$

(3) $a_1 = 0, \quad a_2 = -g, \quad a_3 = g.$

Solution: The initial conditions for equilibrium of the system will be

$$mg - T_{thr} + T_1 = 0,$$

$$mg - T_1 + T_2 = 0,$$

$$mg - T_2 = 0,$$

where T_1, T_2 and T_{thr} are the tensions of springs I and II and the thread respectively. The values of T_1, T_2 and T_{thr} can be found from these equations. The fact that the thread or spring is cut instantaneously implies that T_{thr} or T_2 vanishes. At this instant the equations of the second law of dynamics for the balls become (in the first case)

$$mg + T_1 = ma_1,$$

$$mg - T_1 + T_2 = ma_2,$$

$$mg - T_2 = ma_3,$$

or (in the second case)

$$mg - T_{thr} + T_1 = ma_1,$$

$$mg - T_1 = ma_2,$$

$$mg = ma_3.$$

On solving the system of equations corresponding to each case, we can find the required values of the accelerations of the balls at the initial instant.

117. The acceleration of the wedge is

$$a_1 = \frac{mg \sin 2\alpha}{2(M + m \sin^2 \alpha)};$$

the acceleration of the body is

$$a_2 = \frac{-Mg \sin 2\alpha}{2(M + m \sin^2 \alpha)};$$

the force due to the pressure of the body on the wedge is

$$N = \frac{Mm \cos \alpha}{M + m \sin^2 \alpha} g;$$

the force due to the pressure of the wedge on the horizontal plane is

$$R = \frac{M(m + M)g}{M + m \sin^2 \alpha}.$$

Solution: We draw the forces acting on each body (Fig. 125). The force N alone can communicate acceleration to the wedge in the direction of the x axis (horizontal axis). We write a_1 for the acceleration of the wedge M, a_2 for the horizontal, and a_3 for the vert-

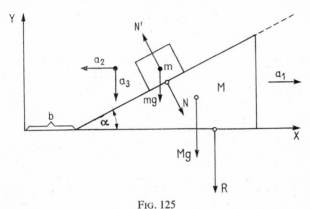

FIG. 125

ical component of the acceleration of the body m. The equations of dynamics now give:

$$N \sin \alpha = Ma_1, \quad mg - N \cos \alpha = ma_3;$$

$$N' \sin \alpha = ma_2, \qquad\qquad |N| = |N'|.$$

The accelerations a_1, a_2, a_3 are also connected by a kinematic relationship, following from the condition that the body m slides over the face of the wedge. This relationship can be obtained thus: let x, y be the coordinates of a point of the body m on the surface in contact with the wedge M; the point lies on the line

$$y = \tan \alpha(x - b).$$

Since x and b vary during the motion, whilst α remains constant, we can differentiate this equation twice: $\ddot{y} = \tan \alpha(\ddot{x} - \ddot{b})$; it may easily be seen that $\ddot{y} = -a_3$, $\ddot{x} = -a_2$ and $\ddot{b} = a_1$; thus the required relationship is $a_3 = \tan \alpha(a_2 + a_1)$. If we solve simultaneously the equations of dynamics and use the relationship obtained between the accelerations, the answers quoted above are obtained.

§ 3. STATICS

118. $F = P - Q$ (Q must be $\leqslant P$).

119. $H = h + \dfrac{\dfrac{l}{2} p}{\sqrt{4P^2 - p^2}} \approx 5 \cdot 5 \,\mathrm{m}.$

120. If the cable were inextensible and the supports absolutely rigid, it would actually be possible for an arbitrarily small force to break the cable; but the fact that the cable is capable of at least small extension and that the supports can deform implies a definite restriction of the tension that a small force can produce in the cable.

121. A compression of 5 kg on the girder AB; a stretching force $\approx 7 \cdot 1$ kg on the wire CB.

122. $Q = 4\sqrt{5}$ kg, $F = 4\left(\sqrt{5 + 2\sqrt{5}} + \sqrt{5 - 2\sqrt{5}}\right)$ kg,

and is inclined to the vertical at an angle $\alpha = \arctan \frac{1}{2}\sqrt{5} - 1$ towards the hook A.

123. $k \geqslant \tan 15° = 0 \cdot 176$.

124. $f = 22 \cdot 5$ kg, $F = 37 \cdot 5$ kg, $(P_2)_{\max} = 180$ kg.

Hint: Let f_a be the tension of the piece a of the rope, f_b the tension of the piece b and so on. Then $f_a = f_b = f$ and $f_c = f_d = 2f$. The equilibrium conditions are $P_1 + P_2 = f_a + f_b + f_d = 4f$.

125. $F = 200$ kg, $T = 1000$ kg.

126. $d = \dfrac{pl}{p_k h} \sqrt{D^2 - h^2} \approx 0 \cdot 05$ cm.

127. $k_{\min} = \frac{1}{2}$, $F > \frac{1}{2}P$, where P is the weight of the cube.

128. $d = \dfrac{2}{\pi} R.$

129. $d = \dfrac{4}{3}\dfrac{R}{\pi}$.

130. $x_c = \dfrac{3\pi + 16}{3\pi + 12} R$.

131. $x_c = \dfrac{2}{3}\dfrac{R\sin^3\alpha}{\alpha - \cos\alpha\sin\alpha}$, where x_c is the distance from the centre.

132. $d = \dfrac{8}{3}\dfrac{R}{\pi}$.

133. $R = 21P$; $\quad x = \dfrac{8a}{7}$; $\quad y = \dfrac{\sqrt{3}a}{7}$.

134. $T = \dfrac{3p}{32}$.

Hint: We can assume that each hemisphere is acted on by two forces of equal magnitude T, applied at the points where the string passes from one hemisphere to the other; since the distance of the centre of gravity of a hemisphere from its centre is $3R/8$, the equation of moments gives $(p/2)(3R/8) = 2TR$.

135. (1) $T_{AB} = \dfrac{F}{2}\left(\dfrac{\cos\alpha\tan\beta}{\cos\gamma} + \dfrac{\sin\alpha}{\sin\gamma}\right)$,

$$T_{AC} = \dfrac{F}{2}\left(\dfrac{\cos\alpha\tan\beta}{\cos\gamma} - \dfrac{\sin\alpha}{\sin\gamma}\right), \quad T_{AD} = \dfrac{F\cos\alpha}{\cos\beta}.$$

(2) $\tan\alpha = \tan\beta\tan\gamma$, and the force F lies in the plane formed by AB and AD.

136. No, since there is no force which would balance the moment of the gravity force about the edge B.

137. $F = \dfrac{\sqrt{10}}{4} T$, the component directed downwards being $3T/4$, and that directed from the wall $T/4$.

138. $T = F = \dfrac{l}{2h}(P + p) = 900$ kg.

Hint: Since there is no friction at the supports, we have $F = T$; these forces form a couple, the moment of which is $M = T \cdot h$ and balances the moments of the gravity forces about the supports.

139. $f = 1$ kg in both cases.

§ 4. WORK, POWER, ENERGY

140. The work $A = 200$ kgm. The potential energy $U = 100$ kgm. Half the work goes into increasing the kinetic energy of the rising load.

141. 0·06 kgm and 0·038 kgm.

142. 4·25 m; $\approx 8·16$ m sec^{-1}.

143. $\dfrac{\partial}{\partial s}\left(\dfrac{mv^2}{2}\right) = mv\,\dfrac{\partial v}{\partial t}\,\dfrac{\partial t}{\partial s} = m\,\dfrac{\partial v}{\partial t} = F.$

144. The work $A \approx 4·3 \times 10^5$ kgm.

145. $U = 0·6$ kgm.

146. 1 kgm.

147. $W = \dfrac{1000}{75}\, Svhg$ h.p.

148. $W = \dfrac{mv_0^3}{4l}.$

149. (1) $U = mgl(1 - \cos \alpha).$

(2) $A = \displaystyle\int_0^\alpha mal \cos \alpha \, d\alpha = mal \sin \alpha.$

(3) On equating the work done by the inertia force to the potential energy of the plumb-line, inclined at an angle α, we find that $g(1 - \cos \alpha_{\max}) = \alpha \sin \alpha_{\max}$, whence we easily obtain

$$\tan \frac{\alpha_{\max}}{2} = \frac{a}{g} \quad \text{or} \quad \alpha_{\max} = 2 \arctan \frac{a}{g}.$$

(4) On comparing the result obtained with the result of Problem 82, we find that in fact $\alpha_{max} = 2\alpha_0$, since

$$\alpha_0 = \arctan \frac{a}{g}.$$

(5) After setting the plumb-line free, it first deflects through the angle α_{max}, then starts to oscillate between the direction determined by this angle and the vertical, i.e. about the direction determined by the angle α_0. The oscillations are gradually damped and the plumb-line remains in the position given by this angle. In this position the sum of the forces acting on the plumb-line is equal to ma and the plumb-line moves with the truck.

150. 330 m.

Solution: When the train brakes (deceleration a) the plumb-line starts to oscillate (see the solution of the previous problem) and deflects a maximum angle $2a/g = 3°\pi/180° = 0.052$, consequently, $2a = 0.51 \text{ m sec}^{-1}$,

$$S = \frac{v^2}{2a}.$$

151. $v = \sqrt{2gR} = 11.2 \text{ km sec}^{-1}$, where R is the radius of the terrestrial sphere.

152. In view of the fact that the gravitational field is lamellar and all mechanical processes are reversible in it, a rocket whose initial velocity exceeds the value found in the previous problem will obviously overcome the earth's gravitational force and pass into interplanetary space.

153. $T \approx \dfrac{mgR}{1 + \dfrac{h}{R}} \approx 6.2 \times 10^9 \text{ kgm}$, R is the radius of the earth

and g the acceleration due to gravity at the earth's surface.

154. $W = pv(k \cos \alpha + \sin \alpha)$.

155. *Solution:* The equation of motion of the boat is of the form $mdv/dt = -rv^2$. On multiplying both sides by the element of the path dS, we obtain on the right the element dA of the work done by the resistance over the path dS:

$$m \frac{dv}{dt} \cdot dS = -rv^2 dS = -r \frac{v_0^2 m^2 dS}{(m + rv_0 t)^2} = dA$$

or

$$mvdv = d\left(\frac{mv^2}{2}\right) = -r \frac{v_0^2 m^2 v dt}{(m + rv_0 t)^2} = -r \frac{v_0^3 m^3 dt}{(m + rmv_0 t)^3}.$$

On integrating these equations under the conditions $v = v_0$ at $t = 0$ and $v = 0$ ax $t \rightarrow \infty$, we find that the right-hand side of the equation is also equal to $\frac{1}{2}mv_0^2$, which is what we wished to prove.

156. $U = \frac{\beta x^4}{4}$, where x is the spring deformation.

157. $T = \frac{2250P}{\pi Rn}$ kg.

158. $\frac{\pi n R p}{3000}$ kgm sec^{-1}.

159. Clockwise, since the working part of the belt will sag less and will embrace a greater part of the pulley circumferences than in the case of counter-clockwise revolution, and the coupling of the belt with the pulley will be greater.

§ 5. Laws of Conservation of Momentum and Energy

160. $v = 10$ cm sec^{-1}.

161. $F = \frac{m^2 v^2}{2SM} = 17$ kg, where M and m are the masses of the rifle and bullet.

162. $v = \frac{M}{m} \frac{\sqrt{2gl} \sin \alpha}{\cos \alpha}$.

Hint: This expression for v is easily obtained by applying the law of conservation of momentum to the component of the momentum of the gun and shell along the inclined plane immediately before and after the instant of firing. The impulse of gravity (acting on both bodies) during the short period Δt of firing is negligibly small.

163. $S_2 = 5000$ m.

Solution: The fact that one half of the shell falls to a point below the point of breaking indicates that the entire momentum of the shell at its topmost point has been communicated to the second half. The fact that half the shell falls $19 \cdot 6$ m in 1 sec implies that it has an initial velocity v_0 downwards at the instant of breaking, and hence the second half has the same momentum upwards. Thus the second half has an initial velocity $2v_{\text{hor}}$ in the horizontal direction after breaking (where v_{hor} is the horizontal component of the shell velocity on firing), and v_0 in the vertical direction. The speed v_0 is given by

$$h = v_0\tau + \frac{g\tau^2}{2},$$

where τ is the time taken for the first half to fall. The horizontal component v_{hor} of the velocity is given by the equations $S_1 = v_{\text{hor}}t$ and $h = \frac{1}{2}gt^2$; $v_{\text{hor}} = S_1\sqrt{g/2h}$. The distance from the point where the second half falls to the point of breaking, measured horizontally, can be found from the formula which describes the travel of the shell *in vacuo*:

$$S_2 - S_1 = 2v_{\text{hor}}\left[\frac{h}{g\tau} - \frac{\tau}{2} + \sqrt{\frac{2h}{g} + \left(\frac{h}{g\tau} - \frac{\tau}{2}\right)^2}\right].$$

On replacing v_{hor} by $S_1\sqrt{g/2h}$, we obtain the answer:

$$S_2 = S_1\left\{\sqrt{\frac{2g}{h}}\left[\frac{h}{g\tau} - \frac{\tau}{2} + \sqrt{\frac{2h}{g} + \left(\frac{h}{g\tau} - \frac{\tau}{2}\right)^2}\right] + 1\right\}.$$

164. $v_1 = \dfrac{P_1(v + u) + Pv}{P + P_1}$; $v_2 = v$; $v_3 = \dfrac{P_1(v - u) + Pv}{P + P_1}$.

165. 9 m sec^{-1} and 1 m sec^{-1}.

166. $v = \dfrac{m_1v_1 + m_2v_2}{m_1 + m_2}$; $T = \dfrac{(m_1v_1 + m_2v_2)^2}{2(m_1 + m_2)}$.

167. On condition that $m_1/m_2 > 20$, where m_1 is the mass of the sphere with the smaller energy. The answer is easily obtained from the relationships

$$20m_1v_1^2 = m_2v_2^2, \quad v = \frac{m_1v_1 - m_2v_2}{m_1 + m_2} > 0,$$

where v is the speed of the spheres after impact, v_1 and v_2 are their speeds before impact.

168. $v = 1000 \text{ m sec}^{-1}$ (from the equation $mv = Mv_1$).

169. $F = \dfrac{2Mv}{\tau}$.

170. $F = \dfrac{\Delta m_1 v}{\Delta t} \approx 2500 \text{ kg}$.

where Δm_1 is the mass of the coal and Δt the time in which this mass is loaded on to the tender.

171. The work is

$$F\Delta S' = \frac{\Delta m}{\Delta t} v\Delta S' = \Delta m \cdot v^2,$$

whilst the kinetic energy of the coal is $\frac{1}{2}\Delta m \cdot v^2$, i.e. half as much. When the pieces of coal come in contact with the tender, they first slide along the floor (in the opposite direction to the motion of the tender) and part of the work done by the locomotive is used in overcoming the resultant friction forces. This work (which is transformed into heat) is equal to $\frac{1}{2}\Delta m \cdot v^2$.

172. The extra pressure on the table (over and above the weight of the part of the cable already lying on the table) is due to the momentum losses of the falling elements of the cable when they strike the table. Let an element of cable of mass $dm = \mu dx$ fall on to the table in the element of time dt, where μ is the mass per unit length of the cable and dx is the element of length of the cable. The force exerted by this element on the table will be

$$\Delta F = \frac{dmv}{dt} = \frac{\mu dxv}{dt} = \mu v^2,$$

where v is the velocity with which the element dm reaches the table. But evidently, $v^2 = 2gx$, where x is the length of the part of the cable lying on the table. Hence $\Delta F = 2\mu gx$. The total force acting on the table is therefore $3\mu gx$.

173. The ball leaves the wedge horizontally and continues in a parabola (see Fig. 126).

174. $p = 2mv \cos \alpha$.

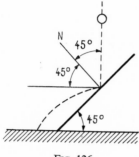

FIG. 126

175. $\Delta T = 2m(v - u) u$; $\Delta p = -2m(v - u)$; the body remains on the wall after impact if:

$$u = \frac{v}{2}.$$

Hint: The laws of elastic impact on the moving wall are easily obtained if we pass to the limit in the formulae for the velocities after impact of two elastic bodies, putting the mass of one body (the wall) equal to infinity.

176. $q = \dfrac{m_2}{m_1 + m_2}$.

177. At the instant when the drum stops, the tension is equal to the weight of the lift, as when the lift is moving; the cable then stretches and the tension gradually increases, until the point when the cage stops. At the instant when the cage stops the tension is a maximum which is greater than the weight of the cage. (It is clear from this that the lift cannot remain fixed in this position; it starts to rise and oscillations of the cage set in.)

The rate of increase of the tension and its magnitude depend on the elastic properties of the cable and the mass of the cage.

178. The elongation ≈ 55 cm, $T \approx 55{,}000$ kg.

179. $h = 0{\cdot}005 \dfrac{M}{m} l.$

180. (1) $v = 2 \dfrac{M + m}{m} \sqrt{lg} \sin \dfrac{\alpha}{2}$;

(2) $v = \dfrac{2M \sqrt{lg} \sin \dfrac{\alpha}{2} - mv'}{m}$;

(3) $v = \dfrac{2M \sqrt{lg} \sin \dfrac{\alpha}{2}}{m}$.

The problem of the impact of a ballistic pendulum (a rigid body revolving about a fixed axis) and a bullet is solved by applying the law of conservation of momentum to the pendulum–bullet system. This method is naturally only permissible when the impact of the bullet is not transmitted to the pendulum axis. This is precisely the situation when the bullet strikes at the so-called centre of oscillation of the pendulum, whose distance from the axis is equal to the reduced length of the ideal pendulum, and the velocity of the bullet is perpendicular to the straight line joining the point of suspension to the oscillation centre. When the impact is at an arbitrary point of the pendulum, the law of conservation of angular momentum has to be applied to the pendulum–bullet system. In the previous case, using the law of conservation of angular momemtum is equivalent to using the law of conservation of momentum. Problems 250 to 252 are similarly concerned with impact on a rigid body mounted on an axis.

181. $\alpha_1 = \dfrac{m_1 - m_2}{m_1 + m_2} \alpha, \quad \alpha_2 = \dfrac{2m_1}{m_1 + m_2} \alpha \sqrt{\dfrac{l_1}{l_2}}.$

182. (1) It describes a parabola above the plane, the height of the vertex being $\frac{1}{2}h$; (2) it slides uniformly along the plane with velocity $\sqrt{gh}$.

183. The box will not move, because the normal p_N and tangential p_t (relative to the inclined plane) components of the momentum p of the vertically incident body will satisfy the relationship $p_N/p_t = \tan \alpha$, which is also satisfied by the components of the weight of the box: $mg_N/mg_t = \tan \alpha = k$, and the box does not move as a result of the action of the latter. After the incident body has come to a complete stop in the box, the increase in the weight of the box does not cause it to move for the same reason.

184. The distance is $Ml/(M - m)$, where M is the mass of the train before uncoupling, and m is the mass of the wagon.

185. $w = \dfrac{Mu}{M + m}$; $\quad v = -\dfrac{mu}{M + m}$.

186. $S_1 = \dfrac{-ml}{M + m}$; $\quad S_2 = \dfrac{Ml}{M + m}$.

187. $a_1 = \dfrac{Ma}{M + m}$; $\quad a_2 = \dfrac{-ma}{M + m}$; $\quad F = -\dfrac{mMa}{M + m}$.

188. (1) $v = \dfrac{-\Delta mu}{M + m}$;

(2) $S_1 = \dfrac{-\Delta ml}{M + 2m + \Delta m}$, $\quad S_2 = \dfrac{(M + 2m)l}{M + 2m + \Delta m}$.

189. $M \dfrac{dv}{dt} = -\mu u$.

Solution: The equation of motion is easily found from the conservation of momentum in the rocket–gas system. On equating the moment of the system at the instant t to the moment at $t + dt$, we get

$$Mv = (M - dM)(v + dv) + dM(v + u).$$

On neglecting second order terms and recalling that $dM = \mu dt$, we obtain the required equation.

190. *Solution:*

$$dv = \frac{-\mu u \, dt}{M} = \frac{-dM}{dt} \frac{u \, dt}{M} = -u \frac{aM}{M} .$$

On integrating the equation under the condition $v = 0$ at $M = M_0$, we obtain $v = u \ln (M_0/M)$, or $e^{v/u} = M_0/M$.

191. (1) $v = -u\left(1 - e^{-\frac{\mu}{M}t}\right)$;

(2) $\eta = 2\left(1 - \frac{|v|}{|u|}\right)\frac{|v|}{|u|}$, $\eta_{max} = \frac{1}{2}$ for $v = \frac{u}{2}$.

Solution: On equating the moments of the system at the instants t and $t + dt$, we obtain

$$Mv = M(v + dv) - (u - v)\mu \, dt. \qquad (1)$$

After integration, we obtain the modulus of the vessel velocity as a function of time. The efficiency of the system is given by the ratio of the useful work (in our case this is the increment of the kinetic energy of the vessel $d(\frac{1}{2}Mv^2) = Mvdv$) to the work of the pump ($\frac{1}{2}\mu dt \cdot u^2$) over equal time intervals:

$$\eta = \frac{2Mv \, dv}{\mu u^2 \, dt} \, ;$$

On using equation (1), we can write:

$$\eta = \frac{2(u - v)v}{u^2} \, .$$

We seek the maximum of this expression as a function of v/u, and obtain

$$\eta_{max} = \frac{1}{2} \quad \text{for} \quad v = \frac{u}{2} \, .$$

§ 6. Dynamics of a Point Particle in Circular Motion

192. (1) $P = mg$; (2) $P = mg - \frac{mv^2}{R}$; (3) $P = mg + \frac{mv^2}{R}$,

where R is the radius of curvature of the bridge.

193. $F = (1 + 4kh) \, mg$; $a = 4 \, kgh$.

Solution: At the low point of its trajectory the ball has an acceleration a_N, directed upwards. Thus the pressure of the ball on the
bottom of the bowl can be written as $F = m(g + a_N)$. The acceleration a_N can be found as follows. Differentiating the equation of the
paraboloid twice with respect to time, we have $\ddot{z} = 2k(\dot{x}^2 + \dot{y}^2)$
$+ 2k(x\ddot{x} + y\ddot{y})$. Hence the required acceleration a of the ball at the
lowest point of its trajectory, where $x = y = 0$, will have the value
$a = \ddot{z}_0 = a_N = 2k(\dot{x}_0^2 + \dot{y}_0^2) = 2kv_0^2$, where

$$v_0^2 = 2gh; \tag{1}$$

thus $\ddot{z}_0 = a_N = 4kgh$. Notice that this method of solution avoids
calculating the radius of curvature of the parabola at its low point,
which must usually be known in order to find the normal acceleration

$$a_N = \frac{v^2}{\varrho}, \tag{2}$$

where ϱ is the radius of curvature of the trajectory. Knowing the
equation of the parabola, we could use differential geometry to find
the value of

$$\varrho = \frac{1}{2k}. \tag{3}$$

Then, by using expressions (1), (2) and (3), the value of a_N could be
found by a different method to that described above.

194. $v_0 = \sqrt{gR} \approx 8 \text{ km sec}^{-1}$, the shell acceleration is equal to g,
and is normal to the trajectory.

195. The shell trajectory is an arc of an ellipse. This curve is
represented by a continuous line in Fig. 127. The remainder of the
ellipse is shown dotted. One focus of the ellipse coincides with the
centre of the earth. The shell acceleration a will always be directed
towards this focus, where $a = \gamma M/R^2$, and γ is the gravitational
constant, M the mass of the earth and R the distance to the centre
of the earth.

196. (1) $H = 5R/2$. (2) The forces acting on the truck are the
gravitational force mg and the pressure of the rails $(mv^2/R) - mg$,
where v is the speed of the truck at this point. (3) If it does not reach
the highest point, the truck leaves the rails and moves along a parabola until it encounters the rails at the low point of the loop.

197. $k = \dfrac{v^2}{Rg} \approx 0.4.$

198. $v = \sqrt{Rg \cot \alpha}.$

199. (1) $\sin \alpha = \dfrac{\omega^2 r_0}{g - \omega^2 l}.$

(2) The trigonometric equation $\omega^2 l \sin \alpha + \omega^2 r_0 = g \tan \alpha$ is solved by using the Fig. 128.

(3) There will be a break in the string at the point where

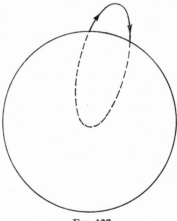

Fig. 127

the extra weight is attached, since the direction of the string, determined by the angle α, depends on l, which is twice as great for one of the weights.

200. $\omega^2 = \dfrac{g}{\sqrt{(R + l)^2 - (R + r)^2}}.$

201. $R = \dfrac{10v^2}{g \sqrt{n(2 + 0.01n)}}.$

202. During the loop the aeroplane has an acceleration $a = v^2/R$ = 9 m sec^{-2}, directed towards the loop centre. At the bottom of the loop the air pressure acting on the wing is

$$m(a + g) = \frac{750}{9.8} (9 + 9.8) \text{ kg} \approx 1.4 \text{ ton,}$$

i.e. the wing loading is almost twice that in horizontal flight. This shows the need for strengthening the structure of an aeroplane for performing the figures of higher pilotage.

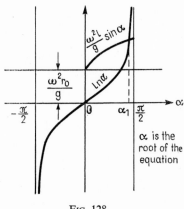

Fig. 128

203. At the bottom of the loop the pilot is pressed to his seat by a force $(80/9.8)(60.5 + 9.8)$ kg ≈ 563 kg, and at the top by a force ≈ 403 kg.

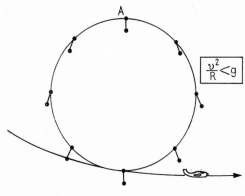

Fig. 129

204. When $v^2/R > g$, the "plumb-line" is directed upwards, when $v^2/R < g$ it is downwards (Fig. 129). The sketch shows the positions of the plumb-line at other points when $v^2/R < g$.

205. The load M occupies either the nearest possible position to the axis, or the most remote. The position at the distance

$$R = \frac{mg}{M\omega^2}$$

from the axis corresponds to an unstable equilibrium, since even when the radius R is increased slightly, the weight mg is insufficient to maintain the mass M on the circle, and it moves away to the most remote point from the axis. Conversely, if R is reduced slightly, the weight mg is greater than the force needed to maintain the mass at the distance R and it approaches the axis.

206. The same answer as in Problem 205.

207. *Solution:* The mass M will perform a motion along the circle of radius $R_0 = mg/M\omega^2$. Since the angular momentum of M must remain constant, we have $M\omega R^2 = N = \text{const}$. Hence it follows that the centrifugal force can be written as

$$f = M\omega^2 R = \frac{N^2}{MR^3}.$$

Figure 130 illustrates the graph of the centrifugal force as a function of R. The constant string tension $F = mg$ acting on the mass M in the opposite direction is represented on the figure by a

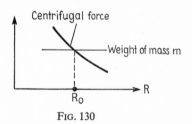

FIG. 130

straight line parallel to the axis of abscissae. The stable position of the mass M on the rotating rod corresponds to the point of intersection of this line with the centrifugal force curve. A deviation in either direction of the mass M from the position R_0 gives rise to a force which returns M to R_0. This means that this position of M is stable. The difference between this result and that of the previous problem is explained by the fact that the angular momentum of the system is assumed constant in the present problem. The entire argument depends on choosing conditions such that R_0 is not small. Otherwise it is impossible to neglect the moment of inertia of the device compared with the moment of inertia of the mass M.

208. Assuming that the mass m is not too large, there are two possible positions of equilibrium: R_{02} (stable) and R_{01} (unstable) (disregarding the position of stable equilibrium $R = 0$ (Fig. 131)). Since in this case the constant angular momentum is $(MR^2 + J_0)\,\omega = a$, the centrifugal force is equal to $Ma^2R/(J_0 + MR^2)^2$. The stability of the equilibrium can be considered by using the graph of the forces, as in the previous answer.

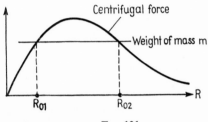

FIG. 131

The existence of two positions of equilibrium of the body on the rod in this case follows at once from the fact that the centrifugal force must tend to zero not only when $R \to \infty$ as in the conditions of the previous problem, but also when $R \to 0$. For, the fact that the system has a moment of inertia J_0 means that, when the mass M approaches the axis of rotation, the speed of rotation remains finite, and the expression $M\omega^2R$ tends to zero as $R \to 0$. A continuous function must have a maximum between two zeros, and hence its graph must cut twice any straight line parallel to the axis of abscissae, which lies below the maximum ordinate of the function. In our present case the graph cuts twice the straight line corresponding to the force mg. The different signs of the derivative at its points of intersection with the line $f = mg$ in fact determine the stability or instability of the positions of equilibrium of the mass M.

209. The string connected to the axis is stretched by a force $\omega^2[m_1R + m_2(R + L)]$; the string joining the masses is stretched by a force $\omega^2m_2(R + L)$.

210. The spring tension must be proportional to its elongation. The coefficient of elasticity of the spring must be $M\omega^2$.

211. $k \approx 48$ gcm^{-1}.

212. Either at the bottom or the top, depending on the value of ω, since the position of equilibrium corresponding to the distance $R = (g/\omega^2)\ CE/ED$ from the axis is unstable. See the answer to Problem 205.

213. $T \approx 1\cdot6P$ kg.

214. The slope is arranged so that the pressure of the train is normal to the plane of the road bed and so that the wheel treads do not tear the rails sideways from the sleepers.

$$\tan \alpha = \frac{v^2}{Rg},$$

where α is the angle of inclination of the road bed to the horizontal, v is the speed of the train and R is the radius of curvature.

215. The floor is the paraboloid of revolution $z = \omega^2(x^2 + y^2)/2g$; the z axis is along the axis of revolution, the origin is at the lowest point, and the x, y axes are in the horizontal plane.

216. (1) The string tension vanishes when its position is given by the angle α (Fig. 48) for which

$$\cos \alpha = \frac{2}{3}.$$

(2) At this point of the trajectory,

$$v = \sqrt{\frac{gL}{3}}.$$

(3) The ball will continue its motion along a parabola until the string is again stretched as a result of the displacement of the ball.

217. *Solution:* The bullet leaves the gun with a velocity directed to the south. It will therefore be acted on by a westwards Coriolis acceleration

$$\frac{d^2x}{dt^2} = 2v\omega \sin \varphi,$$

where ω is the angular velocity of rotation of the earth and φ is the geographic latitude of the firing point. If we regard the bullet velocity vector as constant to a first approximation, double integration over time of the Coriolis acceleration will give us the westward deviation of the bullet from its initial direction as $x = vt^2\omega \sin \varphi = 5\cdot8$ cm.

218. The method of solution will be clear from Fig. 132. The locomotive exerts a force

$$F = 2mv\omega \sin \varphi = 25 \text{ kg},$$

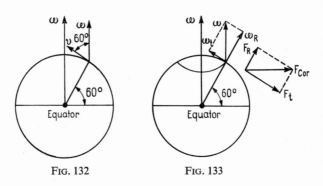

FIG. 132   FIG. 133

on the right-hand (viewed from the direction of travel) rail, where ω is the angular velocity of rotation of the earth about its axis.

219. Figure 133 illustrates the arrangement of the angular velocity and force vectors required for the solution. The train velocity vector is perpendicular to the plane of the figure and is directed away from the reader. The vertical component of the Coriolis force is

$$F_R = 2mv\omega \cos \varphi = 14\cdot9 \text{ kg}.$$

The southwards horizontal component of the Coriolis force is $F_t = 2 mv\omega \sin \varphi = 25\cdot3$ kg, where φ is the geographical latitude.

220. In addition to the gravity force mg, the Coriolis force $f_{Cor} = 2m \, [v \, \wedge \, \omega]$ will act on the falling body. In our case $h = 100$ m, so that $|2[v \, \wedge \, \omega]| \ll g$, and we can take $f_{Cor} = 2mgt\omega$, which is always directed normally to the radius of the earth passing through the initial position of the body at the height h above the earth. As a result of the action of this Coriolis force the body acquires an eastwards acceleration $d^2x/dt^2 = 2gt\omega$. On integrating this equation twice over time with the initial conditions $\dot{x} = 0$ and $x = 0$ at $t = 0$, and using the fact that $t = \sqrt{2h/g}$, we find for the eastwards displacement of the body when it has fallen from the height h:

$$x = \frac{2\sqrt{2}h^{3/2}\omega}{3\sqrt{g}} = 2\cdot2 \text{ cm}.$$

221. (1) In a fixed reference system the deviation of the falling body towards the east (from the vertical through the initial point

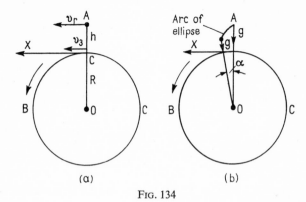

(a)   (b)

Fig. 134

of the body) is explained by the difference in the tangential velocities of points of the earth's surface and of a body at a height h above the earth. The linear velocity of the point C (Fig. 134(a)) produced by the daily rotation of the earth is $v_C = R\omega$, where R is the radius of the earth and ω is its angular velocity of rotation. Similarly, for a body at a height h at the point A, $v_\tau = (R + h)\omega$. Consequently $v_A - v_C = h\omega(1)$. According to the law of inertia, the falling body must retain its initial tangential velocity. During its fall, therefore, the body moves eastwards beyond the point C. This fact was first pointed out by Newton in 1679. When $h \ll R$, the difference (1) between the velocities of the points A and C must, during the time $t = \sqrt{2h/g}$ that the body is falling, lead to an eastward displacement $x = h\omega\sqrt{2h}/\sqrt{g}$ from the point C.

This calculation is only approximate, however. We have assumed that the body moves uniformly in the tangential direction relative to the earth. At the same time, the gravity force will be normal to the initial velocity of the body only at the point A. At subsequent points of the elliptic trajectory (see Problem 195) the gravity force, which is always directed towards the earth's centre, will no longer be perpendicular to the body's velocity and will vary in absolute magnitude as well as direction. Let us carry out the calculation, taking this situation into account. It is easily seen from Fig. 134(b) that the acceleration of the falling body along the x direction is

$$\ddot{x} = -g \sin \alpha \approx -g \frac{x}{R} \approx -g \frac{(R + h)\,\omega t}{R} \approx -g\omega t.$$

On integrating this equation with the initial conditions

$$\left(\frac{dx}{dt}\right)_0 = v_0 = (R + h)\omega$$

when $t = 0$, we obtain the following accurate expression for v_{body}:

$$v_{\text{body}} = \frac{dx}{dt} = -\frac{1}{2}\,g\omega t^2 + (R + h)\omega.$$

The next integration (with the initial conditions $x = 0$ at $t = 0$) gives the value

$$x_{\text{body}} = -\frac{1}{6}\,g\omega t^2 + (R + h)\,\omega t.$$

During the time that the body is falling, the point C on the earth's surface is displaced $x_C = R\omega t$ (when $h \ll R$). As a result the displacement of the body towards the east relative to the point C becomes

$$x_{\text{body}} - x_C = \frac{2\sqrt{2}}{3}\,\frac{h^{3/2}\omega}{\sqrt{g}}.$$

This expression naturally coincides with the result of Problem 220, which was solved in a rotating reference system connected to the earth.

(2) The application to the falling body of the law of conservation of angular momentum is based on the following considerations. A central force of attraction of the earth acts on the body. The angular

momentum of the body relative to the earth's axis must therefore remain fixed. Thus (if we consider a body falling to the equator)

$$m(R + h)^2\omega = m(R + y)^2 \left(\omega + \frac{v}{R + y} \right), \qquad (1)$$

where M is the mass of the body; R is the earth's radius; h is the initial height of the body above the earth; y is the distance of the body from the earth's surface; ω is the angular velocity of rotation of the earth; v is the tangential velocity of the body relative to the earth. On assuming h and $y \ll R$, (1) gives us $v = 2\omega(h - y)$. On the other hand, $h - y = \frac{1}{2}gt^2$. Hence $v = \omega gt^2$. The displacement x of the body from the foot of the perpendicular drawn from its initial position to the earth's surface is

$$x = \int_0^t v \, dt = \omega g \int_0^{\sqrt{\frac{2h}{g}}} t^2 \, dt = \frac{2\sqrt{2}\,\omega h^{3/2}}{3\sqrt{g}}.$$

This elegant solution is due to K. A. Tumanov.

If the experiment is carried out at the geographical latitude φ, a factor $\cos\varphi$ appears in the expression for x.

222. The water surface is at an angle $\alpha = \arctan 2v\omega/g \sin\varphi$ to the horizontal, where v is the speed of flow of the river, ω is the angular velocity of rotation of the earth, g is the acceleration due to gravity. The result is obtained from the condition that the liquid surface be normal to the resultant of the forces applied to it, i.e. the force of gravity and the Coriolis force.

§ 7. DYNAMICS OF A ROTATING RIGID BODY. DYNAMICS OF A SYSTEM

223. $a_2 = -a_1 = \dfrac{m_2 - m_1}{m_2 + m_1 + \dfrac{J}{r^2}} g.$

The string tensions are

$$T_1 = \frac{2m_1 m_2 g + \dfrac{m_1 g J}{r^2}}{m_1 + m_2 + \dfrac{J}{r^2}}; \quad T_2 = \frac{2m_1 m_2 g + \dfrac{m_2 g J}{r^2}}{m_1 + m_2 + \dfrac{J}{r^2}},$$

the stress is

$$T_3 = T_1 + T_2 + Mg.$$

Solution: The tensions T_1 and T_2 in the left and right-hand sections of the string will be different. The equations of the progressive motions of the suspended loads are

$$m_2 g - T_2 = m_2 a_2, \tag{I}$$

$$m_1 g - T_1 = m_1 a_1. \tag{II}$$

The equation of the pulley rotation about its geometrical axis is

$$(T_2 - T_1)r = J \frac{d\omega}{dt}, \tag{III}$$

where $d\omega/dt$ is the angular acceleration of the pulley. Since the string is inextensible and does not slip on the pulley, we have

$$a_2 = -a_1 = r \frac{d\omega}{dt}. \tag{IV,V}$$

The answer is obtained by solving the five equations (I–V), containing the five unknowns a_1, a_2, ω, T_1 and T_2.

224. $\varphi = \dfrac{gt^2}{2R \left(1 + \dfrac{Mg}{2p} \right)}.$

225. $T = \dfrac{Mg}{4 \left(1 + \dfrac{Mg}{2p} \right)}.$

226. $\dfrac{d\omega}{dt} = \dfrac{m_2 R - m_1 r}{m_2 R^2 + m_1 r^2 + J} g;$ $T_1 = m_1 \left(g + r \dfrac{d\omega}{dt} \right);$

$T_2 = m_2 \left(g - R \dfrac{d\omega}{dt} \right).$

227. The weight $\dfrac{mg}{1 + \dfrac{J}{mr^2}}$ must be removed from the pan.

228. If the same weight as in the previous problem is removed from the pan, because the load acceleration is the same (both in magnitude and direction), whether the load is rising or falling.

229. $a = \dfrac{2(P + p)r^2}{pr^2 + PR^2 + 2(P + p)r^2} g$.

230. $a = \dfrac{M + m}{M + m + \dfrac{J}{r^2}} g \approx 196 \text{ cm sec}^{-2}$,

where J is the moment of inertia of the disc and shaft, and M is their mass.

231. *Solution:* Let $\tfrac{1}{2}f_1$ and $\tfrac{1}{2}f_2$ be the tensions of the upper and lower strings. Then the acceleration of the centre of gravity of the coil is $a = (Mg + f_2 - f_1)/M$; the angular acceleration of the coil is $d\omega/dt = (f_2 + f_1) r/J$; the load acceleration is $a_1 = (mg - f_2)/m$. It follows from the kinematic conditions that $a = rd\omega/dt = \tfrac{1}{2}a_1$.

Hence

$$a = \frac{M + 2m}{4m + M + \dfrac{J}{r^2}} g; \quad f_1 = \left(2m + \frac{J}{r^2}\right) a - mg;$$

$$f_2 = m(g - 2a).$$

232. The acceleration of the centre of the lower disc is

$$a_1 = \frac{d^2y}{dt^2} = \frac{1 + \dfrac{3J}{mr^2}}{\dfrac{J}{mr^2} + \left(1 + \dfrac{J}{mr^2}\right)^2} g;$$

of the upper disc, $\quad a_2 = \dfrac{d^2x}{dt^2} = \dfrac{1 + \dfrac{2J}{mr^2}}{\dfrac{J}{mr^2} + \left(1 + \dfrac{J}{mr^2}\right)^2} g$.

Solution: On writing y for the coordinate of the centre of the lower disc, and x for the coordinate of the upper disc centre, ω_1 and ω_2

for the angular velocities of the lower and upper discs, T_1 for the tension of the lower pair of strings, and T_2 for the tension of the upper pair, we can write the following equation of motion and kinematic relationships (the latter follow from the condition that the strings be inextensible):

$$mg + T_1 - T_2 = ma_2, \quad a_2 = \dot{\omega}_2 r, \quad mg - T_1 = ma_1,$$

$$a_1 - a_2 = \dot{\omega}_1 r, \quad T_2 r = J\dot{\omega}_2, \quad T_1 \dot{r} = J\omega_1.$$

On solving these equations simultaneously, we obtain the accelerations.

233. $a = \dfrac{2}{3} g \sin \alpha$ (Fig. 135).

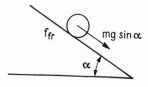

f_{fr} $mg \sin \alpha$

α

FIG. 135

Solution: The equation of motion of the centre of mass of the disc parallel to the inclined plane is

$$mg \sin \alpha - f_{fr} = ma. \tag{1}$$

The equation of the disc rotation about its geometrical axis is

$$J \frac{d\omega}{dt} = f_{fr} R, \tag{2}$$

where $d\omega/dt$ is the angular acceleration of the disc, J is its moment of inertia and R its radius. Since there is no slipping,

$$a = R \frac{d\omega}{dt}. \tag{3}$$

Equations (1), (2) and (3) give us a, $d\omega/dt$ and f_{fr}. Since the disc is solid and uniform, $J = \frac{1}{2}mR^2$. On substituting for J in the expression for a, we obtain the result quoted in the answer.

234. $a = \dfrac{5}{7} g \sin \alpha$.

The friction force is $(2/7) mg \sin \alpha$, where m is the mass of the sphere.

235. $T = Mv^2$, where v is the velocity of the hoop centre.

236. $f = \dfrac{1}{3} mg \sin \alpha = 50 \text{ g}$.

237. $k \geqslant \dfrac{1}{3} \tan \alpha$.

238. (1) The sphere. (2) In the ratio $\sqrt{15/14}$. (3) In the ratio 15/14.

239. The shaft pointed at the end is the more suitable. The friction force is invariable, but the moment of the friction force about the axis is proportional to the radius of the support surface. If kN is the friction force, N the pressure on the support, then, given a uniform distribution of the friction force over the support surface, its moment per unit area will be $2kNR/3$, where R is the radius of the support.

240. $a = \dfrac{m_3 g}{m_1 + \dfrac{3}{2} \cdot 4m_2 + m_3} = 115 \text{ cm sec}^{-2}$.

241. $a = \dfrac{E(R \cos \alpha - r) R}{J + mR^2}$, where J and m are the moment of inertia and mass of the coil respectively; $a > 0$ if $\cos \alpha > r/R$; the friction force $f = F \cos \alpha - ma$.

242. Let f denote the string tension and f' the force of interaction between the frame and the roller. If the roller travels behind, we can write the equations of motion as

$$\frac{3}{2} M_1 a = M_1 g \sin \alpha + f' \quad \text{for the roller}$$

$$M_2 a = M_2 g \sin \alpha - f' + f \quad \text{for the frame.}$$

$M_3 a = M_3 g(\sin \alpha - k \cos \alpha) - f$ for the body of mass M_3. We obtain from these equations:

$$a = \frac{(M_1 + M_2 + M_3) \sin \alpha - kM_3 \cos \alpha}{\dfrac{3}{2} M_1 + M_2 + M_3} \, g,$$

$$f = M_3 g \, \frac{\dfrac{1}{2} M_1 \sin \alpha - k \left(\dfrac{3}{2} M_1 + M_2 \right) \cos \alpha}{\dfrac{3}{2} M_1 + M_2 + M_3}.$$

If $\tan \alpha > k(3 + 2M_2/M_1)$, then $f > 0$. In order for the string to be stretched in this case, the roller must start off behind. If $\tan \alpha < k(3 + 2M_2/M_1)$, the roller must start off in front.

243. $\omega = \sqrt{\dfrac{3g}{l}}$.

Hint. $\dfrac{m}{2l} \displaystyle\int_0^l (\omega x)^2 \, dx = \dfrac{mgl}{2}$, by the law of conservation of energy.

244. $N \approx 52 \times 10^{40}$ g cm^2 sec^{-1}.

245. $1 \cdot 67 \times 10^{11}$ ton $\cdot$ km. For the angular momentum, see the previous answer.

246. The speed of rotation increases up to $(1 + mR^2/J) \, n$ r.p.m. The kinetic energy of the rotation increases by

$$\frac{4\pi^2 n^2 mR^2}{36 \times 10^2 \times 2} \left(1 + \frac{mR^2}{J} \right) \text{erg},$$

if m is in grams and R in centimetres. The increase in energy comes from the work done by the man in moving over the disc.

247. $\omega = \dfrac{mrv}{\dfrac{1}{2} MR^2 + mr^2}$.

248. (1) $\Delta E_k = \dfrac{2J_1^2\omega_1^2}{J_2}$; (2) $\Delta E_k = \dfrac{J_1^2\omega_1^2}{2J_2}$.

249. $\dfrac{d\omega}{dt} = -\dfrac{kg\alpha}{\dfrac{1}{3}pl^2 + 2P\left[\dfrac{2}{5}R^2 + (l + R)^2\right]}$.

250. With the part 2/3 the length of the sabre from its handle.

Solution: Suppose an impact with force F has occurred at a distance r from the mid-point of the sabre, which we regard as a

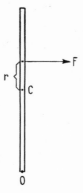

FIG. 136

uniform lamina (Fig. 136). Under the action of this force the lamina starts to move progressively and to rotate; if the point O is to remain at rest, the hand will not feel the impact. We write down the equation of motion of the centre of gravity C of the lamina:

$$m\,\frac{dv}{dt} = F,$$

where dv/dt is the acceleration of the centre of gravity. For the rotation of the lamina relative to the axis through the centre of gravity C,

$$\frac{ml^2}{12}\,\frac{d\omega}{dt} = Fr,$$

where $d\omega/dt$ is the angular acceleration of the lamina, m is its mass and $ml^2/12$ is its moment of inertia relative to C. The point O is at rest if the velocity v of the progressive motion and the linear velocity of O due to the rotation of the lamina about the point C with angular velocity ω are of equal magnitude and in opposite directions, or if

$$\frac{dv}{dt} = \frac{l}{2} \frac{d\omega}{dt}.$$

On substituting this condition in the equation of motion, we get

$$r = \frac{1}{6} l,$$

whence the answer is easily obtained.

The required point on the lamina (sabre) is the so-called centre of impact, which coincides with the centre of oscillation of an ideal pendulum consisting of the same lamina suspended at the point O. Relieving the axis of rotation from the action of the impact is particularly necessary in the case of a ballistic pendulum (see also Problem 180).

251. The lamina will rotate with angular velocity

$$\omega = \frac{12m}{4m + 3m_0} \frac{v}{a},$$

whilst the sphere travels backwards with velocity

$$v_1 = \frac{3m_0 - 4m}{4m + 3m_0} v.$$

252. $v = \dfrac{Ml}{m(l - a)} \sqrt{\dfrac{2lg}{3}} \sin \dfrac{\varphi}{2} \approx 6 \text{ m sec}^{-1}.$

253. The motion of the coupling piece along the rod is given by

$$x = a_0 \cosh \omega t = 2 \cosh 40 \pi t,$$

$$M = 2x \frac{p}{g} \omega v \, \text{g cm} \approx 64 \times 10^5 \sinh 80 \pi t \ \text{dyn cm}.$$

Solution: The motion of the coupling piece is best considered in a rotating system of coordinates. Its equation of motion along the rod under the action of the centrifugal force will now be

$$m \frac{d^2x}{dt^2} = m\omega^2 x.$$

The general solution of this equation is $x = Ae^{\omega t} + Be^{-\omega t}$. On substituting $x(0) = a_0$, $\dot{x}(0) = 0$, we obtain the solution.

The angular momentum of the coupling piece relative to the axis of rotation of the rod is $N = m\omega x^2$; it increases with time. To increase it the external moment

$$M = \frac{dN}{dt} = 2m\omega x \dot{x}.$$

has to be applied.

254. *Solution:* The moments equation for the cylinder rotation about an axis in the plane of rolling will be

$$mR^2 \left(1 + \frac{1}{2} \right) \frac{d\omega}{dt} = FR,$$

where R is the cylinder radius. If the cylinder rolls without slip, its centre of gravity has the horizontal acceleration

$$\frac{dv}{dt} = R \frac{d\omega}{dt},$$

communicated by the friction force; consequently,

$$k \left(g + \frac{F}{m} \right) \geqslant R \frac{d\omega}{dt} = \frac{F}{m \left(1 + \dfrac{1}{2} \right)},$$

where k is the required coefficient of friction.

By hypothesis, $F/m = \frac{1}{2}g$. Hence $dv/dt = g/3$ and $k \geqslant 2/9$.

255. *Solution: Rolling without slip.* The forces acting on the cylinder are shown in Fig. 137. The string tension is F, the friction force f, the load acceleration a. The equation of the progressive motion is: for the cylinder, $F + f = \frac{1}{2}ma$, for the load, $Mg - F$

$= Ma$; the equation of the cylinder rotation is $(F - f) R = \frac{1}{2} m R^2 a / 2R$. Hence we obtain

$$f = \frac{1}{8} ma, \quad F = \frac{3}{8} ma, \quad a = \left(1 + \frac{3}{8} \frac{m}{M}\right)^{-1} g.$$

There will be no slip if $|f| \leqslant kmg$ or $k \geqslant (8 + 3m/M)^{-1}$, where k is the coefficient of friction.

Rolling with slip. The angular acceleration of the cylinder is β, the acceleration of the cylinder axis is b. The equations of motion are now: $F + f = mb$, $(F - f) R = \frac{1}{2} m R^2 \beta$, $Mg - F = Ma$. The

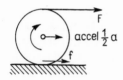

FIG. 137

accelerations are connected by the condition $a = b + \beta R$, and the friction force $f = kmg$. Hence we obtain $a = (1 - km/3M) \times (1 + m/3M)^{-1} g$, on condition that $k < (8 + 3m/M)^{-1}$.

Note: It is useful to consider the motion when $f = 0$ (in the absence of friction).

256. Let f be the force exerted by the rod on the rollers. The equations of motion of the rollers can now be written as follows (the linear and angular accelerations of both rollers are the same): for the first,

$$m \frac{dv}{dt} = mg \sin \alpha + f - F_1, \quad J_1 \frac{d\omega}{dt} = F_1 R;$$

for the second,

$$m \frac{dv}{dt} = mg \sin \alpha - f - F_2, \quad J_2 \frac{d\omega}{dt} = F_2 R;$$

where F_1 and F_2 are the friction forces between the rollers and the plane. In addition, since there is no slip, we have $dv/dt = Rd\omega/dt$.

Hence

$$\frac{d\omega}{dt} = \frac{2Rg \sin \alpha}{\dfrac{J_1 + J_2}{m} + 2R^2} \approx 66 \; \sec^{-2} \quad \text{and}$$

$$f = \frac{J_1 - J_2}{2R} \frac{d\omega}{dt} \approx 0 \cdot 27 \; \text{kg}.$$

Given our choice of signs in the equations of motion, a positive value of f corresponds to the fact that the rod is compressed and pushes the rollers. Consequently, if the roller with the greater moment of inertia is below, the rod is compressed; if it is above, the rod is stretched.

257. *Solution:* Let a be the acceleration of the load m_2, b the acceleration of the support, β the angular acceleration of the cylinder. The string tension is f, the coefficient of friction k.

(1) The equations of motion are

$$F - f = m_2 a, \quad f = (m_1 + m_3)b, \quad fR = \tfrac{1}{2} m_3 R^2 \beta.$$

The condition coonecting the accelerations is $a = b + \beta R$. Hence we find that $a = (\mu + m_2)^{-1} F$, where

$$\mu = (m_1 + m_3)\left(3 + 2\frac{m_1}{m_3}\right)^{-1},$$

$$b = \left(3 + 2\frac{m_1}{m_3}\right)^{-1} a, \quad \beta = 2\left(1 + \frac{m_1}{m_2}\right)\frac{b}{R}.$$

(2) The first two equations of motion are $F - f - km_2 g = m_2 a$, $f - (m_1 + m_3)\, kg = (m_1 + m_3)\, b$, the third is the same as in case (1) and we have the same connection between the accelerations. Hence we obtain:

$$a = (m_2 + \mu)^{-1} F - kg, \quad b = \left(3 + 2\frac{m_1}{m_3}\right)^{-1} a - 2kg\,\frac{\mu}{m_3},$$

$$\beta = \frac{a - b}{R}.$$

(3) $a = (m_1 + m_2)^{-1} F -$ in the absence of friction; $a = (m_1 + m_3)^{-1} F - kg$ in the presence of friction, $\beta = 2F/m_3 R$.

258. The hard-boiled egg rotates as a rigid body, the raw egg as a vessel filled with liquid; when we communicate a rotation to the shell, we do not communicate a rotation to every particle of the liquid.

259. $J \dfrac{d\omega}{dt} = -\dfrac{2\pi\mu a^3 l \omega}{\delta}$, where J is the moment of inertia of the rotor and l is the length of the bearing.

Hence $\omega = \omega_0 \exp\left(-\dfrac{2\pi\mu a^3 l}{\delta J}\right)$, where ω_0 is the initial velocity.

260. *Solution:* A force $F = 0 \cdot 1 P$ acts on the cylinder, which has initially the angular momentum $J\omega_0$. This force communicates angular and linear accelerations to the cylinder:

$$\frac{d\omega}{dt} = -\frac{FR}{J} = -0 \cdot 2 \frac{g}{R} \quad \text{and} \quad \frac{dv}{dt} = g\frac{F}{P} = 0 \cdot 1 g;$$

hence $\omega = \omega_0 - 0 \cdot 2gt/R$ and $v = 0 \cdot 1gt$. The time T is given by the condition $v = \omega R$ or $\omega_0 R - 0 \cdot 2gT = 0 \cdot 1gT$. Hence $T \approx 2 \cdot 14$ sec. When $t > T$ the acceleration is zero.

261. After crossing the boundary the cylinder is first slowed down at a uniform rate then moves with constant velocity; 1/3 the energy is converted into heat, 2/9 into rotatory energy, and 4/9 remains as the energy of the progressive motion.

Solution: Let m be the mass of the cylinder, J its moment of inertia, f the friction force and v_0 the initial velocity. Then

$$m\frac{dv'}{dt} = -f; \quad fr = J\frac{d\omega}{dt},$$

whence

$$v = v_0 - \frac{f}{m}t \quad \text{and} \quad \omega = \frac{frt}{J}.$$

After crossing the boundary the sliding velocity will be $v_{sl} = v - \omega r = v_0 - \alpha ft$, where $\alpha = 1/m + r^2/J = 3/m$ (since $J = \frac{1}{2}mr^2$). After time $T = v_0/\alpha f$ the sliding velocity becomes zero, and pure rolling without slip commences. The speed of the progressive motion in the case of pure rolling is $v_r = v_0 - fv_0/m\alpha f = v_0(1 - 1/m\alpha) = 2v_0/3$. The angular velocity of rolling is $\omega_r = frv_0/J\alpha f = v_0 r/J\alpha$.

Hence $Q_{prog} = \frac{1}{2}mv_0^2(1 - 1/m\alpha)^2$; $Q_{rot} = \frac{1}{2}mv_0^2r^2/m\alpha^2 J$; the energy converted into heat is $Q_{heat} = \frac{1}{2}mv_0^2 - Q_{prog} - Q_{rot} = \frac{1}{2}mv_0^2/m\alpha$. The work done by the friction forces can also be calculated independently; it is found to be $\frac{1}{2}mv_0^2/m\alpha$.

262. $F > F_0$, where $F_0 = (\mu_1 + \mu_2)(m_A + m_B)g$.

Solution: The maximum horizontal acceleration that the body B can have is $a = \mu_2 g$. The force F_0 communicating the acceleration a is given by

$$F_0 - \mu_1(m_A + m_B)g = (m_A + m_B)a;$$

on substituting for a in this, we obtain the answer.

263. (1) The acceleration of the body is

$$a_2 = \frac{M(\sin\alpha - \mu\cos\alpha)\cos\alpha}{M + m(\sin\alpha - \mu\cos\alpha)\sin\alpha}g,$$

of the wedge,

$$a_1 = \frac{m}{M}a_2.$$

(2) The acceleration of the body is

$$a_2 = \frac{M\sin\alpha(\cos\alpha + \mu\sin\alpha)}{M + m\sin\alpha(\sin\alpha - \mu\cos\alpha)}g,$$

of the wedge,

$$a_1 = \frac{m\sin\alpha\cos\alpha - \mu(M + m\cos^2\alpha)}{M + m\sin\alpha(\sin\alpha - \mu\cos\alpha)}g.$$

(3) In the first case $\mu < \tan\alpha$, in the second the condition for motion of the wedge is $\mu < m\sin\alpha\cos\alpha/(M + m\cos^2\alpha)$.

264. $a_{min} = g\dfrac{b}{h}$, where g is the acceleration due to gravity; $N = mg$;

$$x = \frac{ah}{2g}.$$

265. (1) $k_{min} > \dfrac{b}{h}$; (2) if $k < k_{min}$, the car will slide on the bend when $v = \sqrt{bgR/h}$.

266. The cylinder topples over and falls from the disc when the angular velocity of the latter is

$$\omega = \sqrt{\frac{Dg}{Rh}}.$$

267. The analysis cannot be confined to the forces acting on the wheel; the forces acting on the other parts of the locomotive must also be taken into account.

Let us consider separately the forces acting on the wheel and the locomotive (Fig. 138(a)). We shall assume for simplicity that the

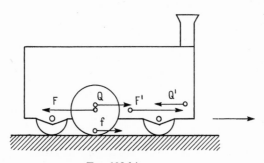

FIG. 138 (a)

locomotive has only one driving wheel. When the drive-gear is above the wheel-axle the locomotive is acted on by a force Q' from the drive-gear and F' from the wheel. The wheel is acted on by a force f from the rails, F from the locomotive and Q from the drive gear. We shall simplify the discussion by assuming that the motion of the locomotive is uniform. By the second law of dynamics, $F = f + Q$, by the third law $Q = Q'$ and $F = F'$. The force $f = F' - Q'$ is applied in a forward direction to the locomotive. When the drive-gear is below the axle (Fig. 138(b)) the force distribution is as follows: the forces applied to the wheel are f, Q and F, and $f + F = Q$ (by the second law of dynamics), whilst the forces applied to the locomotive are f' and Q' [$F' = F$ and $Q' = Q$ (by the third law)], so that the resultant $Q' - f' = f$ i.e. a force directed forwards, is applied to the locomotive.

In the second case, therefore, the wheel axle pushes the locomotive backwards (the force F'), but at the same time the greater force Q' pushes it forwards.

268. $f = \dfrac{r}{R} Q.$

269. The angular velocity of precession is

$$\Omega = \frac{mgl \sin \alpha}{J\omega \sin \alpha} = \frac{mgl}{J\omega},$$

where α is the angle between the top axis and the vertical. The direction of the precession is the same as the direction of rotation of the top.

270. $M = J \dfrac{\pi Nu}{30R} = 62{\cdot}3 \text{ kgm}.$

271. By the law of dynamics, $dN/dt = M$, where N is the angular momentum vector and M is the moment of the force acting on the body. In the present case the moment of the force acting on the

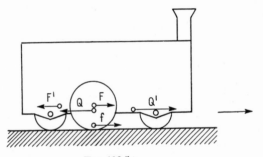

Fig. 138(b)

planet (measured relative to the sun) is $M = [r \wedge F]$, where r is the position vector of the planet, and F the force of attraction that the sun exerts on the planet. Since r and F are directed along the same straight line, we have $M = 0$ and hence $N = $ const. This statement holds for all motions under the action of central forces.

272. *Solution:* The following relationships can be used for the proof:

$$N = [r \wedge mv] = [mr \wedge [\omega \wedge r]] = \left[mr \wedge \left[\frac{d\alpha}{dt} \wedge r \right] \right],$$

where $\omega = d\alpha/dt$ is the angular velocity of the planet, and α is the angle of rotation of its position vector. Using the fact that

$$\left[mr \wedge \left[\frac{d\alpha}{dt} \wedge r \right] \right] = \frac{mr^2 d\alpha}{dt} = 2m \frac{ds}{dt} = 2m\sigma,$$

we obtain the required equation. For, by the rules of vector algebra, the last vector product can be written as $[r \wedge [\omega \wedge r]] = \omega \cdot r^2 -$ $- r(r \cdot \omega) = \omega r^2$, since $r \perp \omega$. But $\omega r^2 \, dt = r^2 \, d\alpha$ is twice the area swept out by the position vector r in time dt. It follows from what was proved earlier (see the previous problem) that $\sigma = $ const. The last relationship amounts to Kepler's second law.

§ 8. GRAVITY

273. $g = \dfrac{4\pi Rkd}{3} \approx 974 \text{ cm sec}^{-2}$.

274. $g = g_0 \left(\dfrac{R}{R + h} \right)^2 \approx 975 \text{ cm sec}^{-2}$.

275. $g_M \approx 162 \text{ cm sec}^{-2}$.

276. $a = \dfrac{4\pi^2 R^3}{T^2 r^2} \approx 28g$, where g is the acceleration due to gravity on the earth's surface.

277. The same as to the earth itself (if the earth's diameter is neglected compared with its distance from the sun), i.e. the acceleration

$$a = \frac{4\pi^2 R}{T^2} \approx 0.6 \text{ cm sec}^{-2},$$

where R is the radius of the earth's orbit and T the period of the revolution of the earth about the sun.

278. $g_{\text{Leningrad}} = g_{\text{Moscow}} \left(1 + 2 \dfrac{\Delta T}{T} \right) = g_{\text{Moscow}}(1 + 0.0008)$,

where ΔT is the difference between the periods T of the oscillation of the pendulum in Moscow and Leningrad.

279. The clock goes about 2·5 times more slowly, since $g_M/g_E \approx$ 0·16 (see Problem 275).

280. $R \approx 785 \cdot 10^6$ km.

281. $g_S \approx \dfrac{4\pi^2 R}{T^2}\left(\dfrac{2}{\alpha}\right)^2 \approx 275$ m sec^{-2}.

282. $D = \sqrt[3]{\dfrac{M\gamma T^2}{4\pi^2}}$, where γ is the gravitational constant.

283. $g = \dfrac{4\pi^2 60^3 R}{T^2} \approx 985$ cm sec^{-2}.

284. $U(R) = \dfrac{mg R_0^2}{R}$, where R_0 is the radius of the earth.

Solution: The gravity force acting on a body at a distance r from the earth's centre is $f = mgR_0^2/r^2$. Thus the potential energy at a distance R is

$$U(R) = \int_\infty^R f\, dr = -\frac{mg R_0^2}{R}.$$

285. $v = v_0 \sqrt{\dfrac{R_0}{R}}$, where $v_0 = \sqrt{gR_0} \approx 7 \cdot 9$ km sec^{-1},

is the velocity of the satellite in a circular orbit (theoretical), the radius of which is equal to the earth's radius R_0.

Hint: The gravitational force exerted by the earth on a satellite of mass m is mgR_0^2/R^2.

286. $R = \sqrt[3]{\dfrac{g}{\omega^2 R_0}}\, R_0 \approx 6 \cdot 61\, R_0$, where R_0 is the earth's radius and $\omega = 2\pi/24 \times 3600$ radian sec^{-1}.

Hint: The centripetal acceleration $\omega^2 R$ of the satellite must be equal to the acceleration communicated to the satellite by the gravitational force gR_0^2/R^2.

287. (1) The first.

(2) $\dfrac{R_1}{R_2} = \dfrac{2gR_0}{v_0^2}$.

Solution: By the law of conservation of energy, we have for the first shell:

$$\frac{v_0^2}{2} - gR_0 = -g\frac{R_0^2}{R_1},$$

since its speed at the highest point is zero, or $R_1 = 2gR_0^2/(2gR_0 - v_0^2)$. See also Problem 284 and its solution. For the second shell, by the law of conservation of energy,

$$\frac{v_0^2}{2} - gR_0 = \frac{v_1^2}{2} - g\frac{R_0^2}{R_2},$$

where v_1 is its speed at the furthest point; in addition, by the law of conservation of angular momentum,

$$v_0R_0 = v_1R_2.$$

Hence we obtain

$$R_2 = \frac{v_0^2R_0}{2gR_0 - v_0^2}.$$

288. $R_1 = \dfrac{R_0}{\mu_1 - 1}$, $R_2 = \dfrac{R_0}{\mu_2 - 1}$,

where $\mu_{1,2} = \dfrac{2gR_0}{(v_0 \pm \omega R_0)^2}$,

ω is the angular velocity velocity and R_0 is the radius of the earth. $R_1 \approx 6 \cdot 8\, R_0$, $R_2 \approx 2 \cdot 52\, R_0$.

Hint: See the solution of Problem 287.

289. $v_c = \sqrt{2gR_0} \approx 11 \cdot 2\ \text{km sec}^{-1}$.

The velocity can be at any angle to the vertical.

Solution: By the law of conservation of energy, $\frac{1}{2}mv_c^2 - mgR_0 = 0$. The potential energy at the earth's surface (see Problem 284) is $-mgR_0$, whilst at an infinite distance the kinetic and potential energies are both zero.

290. $v_2 = v_1 \dfrac{h}{l} = 54 \cdot 6 \text{ km sec}^{-1}$.

291. *Solution:* We imagine a particle at a point A of space (Fig. 139), surrounded by an indefinitely thin spherical layer of material. We draw from A a cone of indefinitely small angle, shown sectionally in Fig. 139. The cone cuts areas $d\sigma_1$ and $d\sigma_2$ from the layer. The normals to both areas form the same angle with the axis of the cone, so that $d\sigma_1/r_1^2 = d\sigma_2/r_2^2$. Since the layer is uniform, the gravitating masses inside the cone are proportional to $d\sigma_1$ and $d\sigma_2$, so that the resultant attraction exerted by these masses on a particle at A is zero.

The entire spherical surface can evidently be split up by such cones, so that the gravitational force at A due to the entire layer is zero. Any uniform spherical layer can be imagined as consisting of indefinitely thin spherical layers, so that the gravitational force in an interior cavity of a uniform spherical layer is zero.

The answer is still the same if the density of the material in the spherical layer depends on the radius.

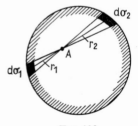

FIG. 139

292. *Solution:* We split the sphere into two parts by means of a sphere of radius r (Fig. 140). If the body (point) is situated on the boundary of these two parts, the gravity force due to the outer part is zero (see the answer to Problem 291), whilst the gravity force due to the inner part is proportional to r^3 (the mass is proportional to the volume of the sphere), and inversely proportional to r^2. Thus the gravity force acting on a particle of mass m is $f = kmr$, where k is a coefficient of proportionality. Since this formula must hold for any r and, in particular, for $r = R_0$, we have $f = kmR_0 = mg$; hence we find that $k = g/R_0$ and obtain the required result:

$$f = \frac{mgr}{R_0}.$$

293. $U(r) = \frac{mgr^2}{2R_0} - \frac{3}{2} mgR_0$, where m is the mass of the body
and r its distance from the centre of the earth.

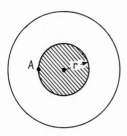

FIG. 140

Solution: Inside the shaft the gravitational force is (see Problem 292) $f = mgr/R_0$, hence

$$U(r_1) - U(0) = \int_0^{r_1} f\,dr = \frac{mgr_1^2}{2R_0},$$

or

$$U(r_1) = U(0) + \frac{mgr_1^2}{2R_0}.$$

We can choose $U(0)$ so that the potential energy given by the formula quoted in Problem 284 is the same as that obtained on the earth's surface when $r_1 = R_0$; now,

$$U(R_0) = U(0) + \frac{mgR_0}{2} = -mgR_0,$$

or

$$U(0) = -\frac{3}{2} mgR_0.$$

294. $v = \sqrt{gR_0} = 7 \cdot 2 \text{ km sec}^{-1}$.
Hint: See Problem 293.

295. All the bodies in the shell are in the same gravitational field as the shell itself, and therefore undergo the same acceleration as the shell; hence a body suspended from a spring balance fixed relative to the shell does not cause an extension of it. The mass of the body may be measured by the following method. The spring can be used to communicate a certain acceleration relative to the shell, and the mass can be determined from the ratio of the force (measured from the spring extension) to the acceleration (the mass of the shell is assumed very much greater than the mass of the measured body).

296. The balance indicates the "weight" $p = ma$ dyne $= ma/g$ g. The spring balance suspended in the shell will stretch in this case in the opposite direction to the shell's deceleration (due to the resistance of the planet's atmosphere).

297. If there were no air resistance the equipment in the shell would cease to record the existence of a gravity force when the shell left the mouth of the gun. Because of the air resistance the shell acquires an extra negative acceleration, and the equipment in the shell records a "gravity" force in the opposite direction to the acceleration to which the shell is subjected, i.e. in the direction of the shell's motion.

298. The linear velocity of an orbiting satellite is inversely proportional to the square root of its distance from the central body.

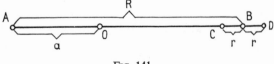

Fig. 141

Whereas the linear velocity of the elements of a continuous ring is directly proportional to their distance from the central body.

299. *Solution* (see Fig. 141): Let O be the centre of mass of the bodies A and B. The fixed distance between A and B will only be preserved when they rotate with angular velocity $\omega = (1/R) \sqrt{\gamma(M_A + M_B)/R}$ about the point O. The conditions for equilibrium of bodies C and D may be written in a rotating coordinate system (fixed to A and B) as

$$M_C \left\{ -\frac{\gamma M_A}{(R-r)^2} + \omega^2(R-a-r) + \frac{\gamma M_B}{r^2} \right\} + F_C = 0,$$

$$M_D \left\{ -\frac{\gamma M_A}{(R+r)^2} + \omega^2(R-a+r) - \frac{\gamma M_B}{r^2} \right\} + F_D = 0,$$

where the direction from A to B is taken as positive, F_C and F_D are the required forces and γ is the gravitational constant. On eliminating ω, using the relationship $a\omega^2 = \gamma M_B/R^2$ and neglecting higher order terms with respect to r/R, we finally obtain:

$$F_C = \gamma M_C \left\{ -\frac{M_B}{r^2} + \frac{r}{R^3}(3M_A + M_B) \right\},$$

$$F_D = \gamma M_D \left\{ \frac{M_B}{r^2} - \frac{r}{R^3}(3M_A + M_B) \right\},$$

i.e. when $M_C = M_D$ either force is less than the force of attraction of the corresponding mass by the body B, the difference being the same in either case.

300. *Solution:* In Problem 299 we can regard A as the centre of the sun and M_A as its mass, B as the centre of the earth and M_B as the earth's mass, C and D as two positions of the same body of mass $M_C = M_D$ on the earth's surface (C in the day, D in the night). It follows from the solution of Problem 299 that a body will always weight slightly less at midnight and noon than in the morning and evening. But it may easily be seen that this difference in weight is very much less than the force of attraction of the sun, since the latter ($\gamma M_C M_A/R^2$) is multiplied by the very small quantity $3r/R$. (The earth's mass M_B can be neglected compared with $3M_A$, where M_A is the sun's mass, when estimating the weight changes).

301. The pattern of Problem 299 can be used to explain the occurrence of tides due to the moon. The moon A and earth B rotate about a common centre of gravity O. At the points C and D on the earth's surface, where the water "weighs" less than at all other points, water "humps" are formed. To calculate the tide-forming forces, we substitute the masses of the moon and earth respectively for M_A and M_B. We then use the formulae obtained in Problem 299 (since the mass of the moon can be neglected compared with that of the earth) to find approximately the weight of a body of mass M at the points of the earth's surface nearest to and furthest from the moon:

$$Mg \approx Mg_0 \left[1 - 3 \left(\frac{r}{R} \right)^3 \frac{M_A}{M_B} \right],$$

where g_0 is the acceleration communicated by the earth, r is the earth's radius, R the distance from the centre of the earth to the centre of the moon.

302. The point at which $G = 0$ divides the straight line joining the centres of these planets in the ratio 9:1, i.e., it lies at a distance $\approx 36.7 \times 10^3$ km from the surface of the moon.

303. $A \approx 5.4 \times 10^6$ kgm.

Solution. The minimum work in displacing a mass m from the earth to the moon can be written thus: $A \approx mR_{\text{Earth}} g_{\text{Earth}} - mR_{\text{Moon}} g_{\text{Moon}}$, where R_{Earth} and R_{Moon} are the radii of the earth and moon respectively, and $g_{\text{Earth}}, g_{\text{Moon}}$ the accelerations due to gravity on the surfaces of the earth and moon, caused by the gravitational forces of these planets (see the solution of Problem 287).

§ 9. Elastic Deformations

304. $p = 2450$ kgcm^{-2}.

305. No. The length of a cylinder which cannot support its own weight is $l = p/\gamma$, where p is the breaking strain, γ is the specific weight of the material; $l = 175$ m.

306. $p = E\alpha(t_1 - t_2)$; $p_{\text{winter}} \approx +1000$ kgcm^{-2} (extension) and $p_{\text{summer}} \approx -375$ kgcm^{-2} (compression).

307. $D = 27$ mm.

308. $\Delta v = \dfrac{1 - 2\mu}{E} lP$, where E is Young's modulus and μ is Poisson's coefficient. ($\Delta v < 0$ in the case of compression and $\Delta v > 0$ in the case of extension).

309. $Q = \dfrac{3\sqrt{3}}{2}\, a^2 p \approx 11\ 677{\cdot}5$ kg.

310. $\varDelta l = \dfrac{dl^2}{2E}$, where d is the specific weight of the rod material, l is its length, E is the modulus of elasticity; the volume increase is $\varDelta v = (1 - 2\mu)\, v_0^2 d/2SE$, where v_0 is the initial volume, μ is Poisson's coefficient, S is the cross-sectional area.

311. $\varDelta l_1 = 2\varDelta l_2 = \dfrac{4P}{k_2 + 4k_1}$, $\quad P_1 = \dfrac{4k_1}{k_2 + 4k_1}\, P,$

$$P_2 = \dfrac{2k_2}{k_2 + 4k_1}\, P.$$

312. The rope deformations (elongations) are shown enlarged in Fig. 142. 1, 2 and 3 are the numbers of the ropes, α is the angle between each pair. If the length of the middle rope is L, the elongation of the first and third is $\varepsilon_1 = \varepsilon_3 = (\varDelta l_1/L) \cos \alpha$, of the second $\varepsilon_2 = \varDelta l_2/L = \varDelta l_1/L \cos \alpha$. The tension $\sigma = E\varepsilon$ for each rope, E is Young's modulus for the material. Hence $\sigma_1 = \sigma_3 = \sigma_2 \cos^2 \alpha$.

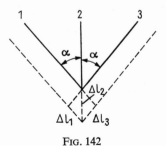

Fig. 142

313. If P_2 is the tension in the middle rope, P_1 the tension in the side ropes, and α the angle between the ropes,

$$P_1 = \dfrac{P \cos^2 \alpha}{1 + 2 \cos^3 \alpha}\ ; \quad P_2 = \dfrac{P}{1 + 2 \cos^3 \alpha}.$$

Note: It is useful to consider the case when the cross-section of the middle rope is half that of the side ropes.

314. $P_1 = \dfrac{P}{2}\,\dfrac{6\alpha_2 + \alpha_3}{\alpha_1 + 4\alpha_2 + \alpha_3}$; $\quad P_2 = \dfrac{P}{2}\,\dfrac{3\alpha_1 + \alpha_3}{\alpha_1 + 4\alpha_2 + \alpha_3}$,

$$P_3 = \dfrac{P}{2}\,\dfrac{2\alpha_2 - \alpha_1}{\alpha_1 + 4\alpha_2 + \alpha_3}, \quad \text{where} \quad \alpha_1 = \dfrac{1}{S_1} ;$$

$$\alpha_2 = \dfrac{1}{S_2} ; \quad \alpha_3 = \dfrac{1}{S_3} .$$

All the rods are strained when $S_1 > \tfrac{1}{2}S_2$.

Solution: If Δx_1 is the elongation of the first rod and Δx_3 of the third, we can write the following equations: (1) $P = AS_1\Delta x_1$; (2) $P_2 = AS_2\tfrac{1}{2}(\Delta x_1 + \Delta x_3)$; (3) $P_3 = AS_3\Delta x_3$, where A is a definite constant. We can add two further equations: (4) $P_1 + P_2 + P_3 = P$ is the equation of the equilibrium of the forces, and (5) $P_1 = P_2 + 3P_3$ is a consequence of the equality of the moments. The answer is obtained by solving these equations.

315. $P = 125$ kg, $\lambda = 5$ mm.

Hint: (1) If the maximum tension in the rod cross-section at the point of constraint is σ, the distribution of the normal stresses in

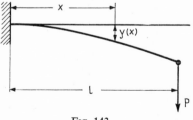

Fig. 143

this cross-section is described by $2\sigma z/a$, where a is the height of the cross section and z is the distance from the mid-point of the section. The fact that the moment Pl of the external forces is equal to the moment of the internal forces can now be written as

$$Pl = \dfrac{4\sigma b}{a} \int_0^{\frac{a}{2}} z^2\, dz = \dfrac{\sigma b a^2}{6},$$

where b is the width of the rod section.

(2) The bending curve of a clamped cantilever (Fig. 143) is given by the differential equation

$$P(l - x) = EJ \frac{d^2y}{dx^2},$$

where $P(l - x)$ is the moment of the external forces about the section having the coordinate x, J is the moment of inertia of the cross-sectional area about the horizontal axis through the centre of gravity of the section. For a rectangle of height a and width b, $J = a^3b/12$. The bending equation can be integrated twice, using the conditions

$$y(0) = \frac{dy}{dx}(0) = 0.$$

Now,

$$\frac{dy}{dx} = \frac{P}{EJ} \int_0^x (l - \xi)\, d\xi = \frac{P}{EJ}\left(lx - \frac{x^2}{2}\right),$$

$$y(x) = \frac{P}{EJ} \int_0^x \left(l\xi - \frac{\xi^2}{2}\right) d\xi = \frac{P}{2EJ}\left(lx^2 - \frac{x^3}{3}\right),$$

whence $\lambda = y(l) = Pl^3/3EJ$; on substituting for J, we get

$$\lambda = \frac{4Pl^3}{a^3bE} = 5 \text{ mm}.$$

316. $\lambda = \dfrac{Pl^3}{48EJ}$.

Hint: The sag can be calculated from the formula given in the previous answer, if we note the fact that the cross-section at the mid-point of the beam does not turn during the deformation. The bending is thus the same as for half the beam clamped as a cantilever, with the support reaction, which is equal to $\frac{1}{2}P$, acting at the end of the beam.

317. *Solution:* Let the displacement of the end of the rod be Δl. Under the action of the force P_2 from the central spring the beam bends upwards by the amount δ. The rod will now be in equilibrium under the action of the forces shown in Fig. 144, where $P_1 = k_1\Delta l$, $P_2 = k_2(\frac{1}{2}\Delta l - \delta)$. Assuming that Δl is very small, we can find δ

from the formula given in the previous answer, or $\delta = (P - P_1)l^3/24EJ$. The condition that the moments of the forces be equal is: $\frac{1}{2}lP_2 + P_1l = Pl$.

We find from these equations:

$$\Delta l = \frac{4 + 2\alpha}{4 + \beta + 2\alpha} \cdot \frac{P}{k_1},$$

where $\alpha = k_2l^3/24EJ = \dfrac{\text{stiffness of central spring}}{\text{flexural rigidity of half the beam}}$ and

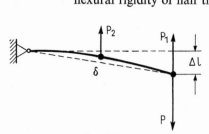

FIG. 144

$\beta = k_2/k_1$. On eliminating Δl and δ, we obtain the answer:

$$P_1 = \frac{4 + 2\alpha}{4 + \beta + 2\alpha} P,$$

$$P_2 = \frac{2\beta}{4 + \beta + 2\alpha} P \quad \text{and} \quad \frac{\Delta l}{2} - \delta = \frac{2}{4 + \beta + 2\alpha} \frac{P}{k_1}.$$

Examine the case of an absolutely rigid rod $\alpha = 0$ and the case of an ideally flexible mod $\alpha = \infty$.

318. $\lambda = \dfrac{Pl^3}{2ab^3E} \approx 0.03$ mm (see the hint on Problem 316).

319. $\lambda = \dfrac{Pl^3}{4a^4E} \approx 1.25$ mm.

320. Since the moment of inertia of the rod section is $J = \pi(D^4 - d^4)/64$, we have

$$\lambda = \frac{4Pl^3}{3\pi(D^4 - d^4)E} \approx 1.6 \text{ mm}.$$

321. $E = \dfrac{4Pl^3}{3\pi R^4 \lambda} \approx 10^4$ kg mm^{-2} (see the moment of inertia in the previous answer).

322. $E_1 = \dfrac{1}{48} \dfrac{Pl^3}{\pi R^4 \lambda}$.

Hint: The sag can be calculated from the formula of Problem 316, if we observe that, as a result of symmetry, each quarter of the beam can be regarded as being clamped like a cantilever (Fig. 145).

This is possible because the bending moment is zero at the points where we have imagined the beam to be divided. As a result of symmetry the curvature at these points is zero, so that the bending moment is also zero.

323. We assume that the rod section at a distance dl from the other section is turned through an angle $d\varphi$ relative to it as a result

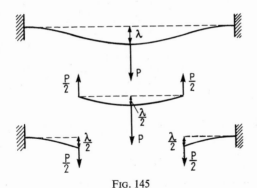

Fig. 145

of the bending. The ring cut out between these sections, of radius ϱ and thickness $d\varrho$, will turn through the angle (Fig. 146)

$$d\alpha = \frac{\varrho \, d\varphi}{dl}.$$

The tangential stress in the section, at a distance ϱ from its axis, will be

$$\tau = N\frac{\varrho \, d\varphi}{dl}.$$

The moment of the forces acting on the surface of the ring of radius ϱ and thickness $d\varrho$, is

$$dM = 2\pi\varrho d\varrho \cdot \tau\varrho = 2\pi N \frac{d\varphi}{dl} \varrho^3 d\varrho.$$

The moment of the forces in the section is

$$M = 2\pi N \frac{d\varphi}{dl} \int_0^r \varrho^3 d\varrho = \pi N \frac{d\varphi}{dl} \frac{r^4}{2},$$

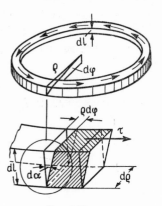

FIG. 146

where r is the rod radius. The moment M is equal to the moment of the external forces; hence

$$M = 2PR.$$

On substituting this in the previous expression, we get

$$\frac{d\varphi}{dl} = \frac{4PR}{\pi Nr^4},$$

and consequently,

$$\varphi = \frac{4PRl}{\pi Nr^4},$$

$$\varphi = \frac{1}{5\pi} \approx 3\cdot6°.$$

324. When the shaft rotates the centre of mass of the disc describes a circle of radius $d + \xi$, where ξ is the sag of the shaft, which depends on its speed of rotation. The elastic force $k\xi$ communicates a centrifugal acceleration to the centre of mass. We can therefore write $m\omega^2(d + \xi) = k\xi$, whence the bending is

$$\xi = \frac{d}{\dfrac{k}{m\omega^2} - 1} \text{ mm.} \tag{1}$$

The angular frequency $\omega = \sqrt{k/m}$, for which $\xi \to \infty$, is known as the critical frequency, and an attempt must obviously be made to arrange the conditions so that the shaft does not operate at its critical frequency. The shaft may operate above the critical frequency. In this case it must be accelerated in such a way that it passes rapidly through the critical frequency. The amplitude of the shaft vibrations is then unable to increase substantially.

325. $v = k\sqrt{F/\varrho}$, where k is a dimensionless coefficient whose value cannot be found from the method used for solving the problem.

Hint: $[F] = MLT^{-2}$; $[\varrho] = ML^{-1}$, $[v] = LT^{-1}$, where M is the mass, L the length and T time.

We have

$$v = f(F, \varrho), \quad \text{or} \quad [v] = [F^m \varrho^n], \quad LT^{-1} = (MLT^{-2})^m \cdot (ML^{-1})^n,$$

whence we obtain the following equations for the respective degrees of T, L and M in the expressions for the dimensionality of the velocity:

$$m - n = 1, \quad 2m = 1, \quad m + n = 0,$$

whence we find that

$$m = +\frac{1}{2}; \quad n = -\frac{1}{2}.$$

326. 0·4 g.

327. $v = k\sqrt{\dfrac{E}{\varrho}}$.

Hint: Make use of the hints for the solution of Problem 325.

328. $\lambda = \dfrac{l}{2} \sqrt[3]{\dfrac{4P}{\pi d^2 E}}.$

329. We have from the similarity of the triangles (Fig. 147), $\Delta l/\frac{1}{2}d \approx 2l/(D + d)$ for $D \gg l$, whence $\Delta l/l = d/(D + d)$. The tension produced in the upper part of the wire as a result of its elongation is

$$\sigma = E \frac{\Delta l}{l} = E \frac{d}{D + d} = 2 \cdot 10^4 \times \frac{1}{2000} = 10 \,\mathrm{kg mm^{-2}}.$$

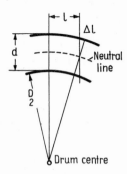

FIG. 147

330. The shortening of the beam is halved.

Solution: In the absence of a support the beam will be set in accelerated motion. The force of compression in the section at a distance x from A will be $T = F(1 - x/L)$, since the preceding elements of the beam must communicate the acceleration to those that follow. The change in length of the element dx at a distance x from A will be

$$d\xi = \frac{T}{ES} \, dx = \frac{F}{ES} \left(1 - \frac{x}{L} \right) dx.$$

The total change in length is therefore

$$\Delta L = \int_0^L d\xi = \frac{1}{2} \frac{LF}{ES}.$$

331. There will be no stress, since in this case the earth's gravitational force acts on all the elements of the beam, communicating the same acceleration to them. In the previous problem the force was applied to one end of the beam, and the more remote elements acquired acceleration because of the compression of those nearer.

332. $F = \dfrac{\beta}{2}\,\dfrac{r^2}{2\pi R^2}\,M.$

333. $T = \dfrac{M\omega^2}{2L}\,(L^2 - x^2);\quad \Delta L = \dfrac{M\omega^2}{3ES}\,L^2,$

where x is the distance of the section in question from the axis of rotation.

§ 10. VIBRATIONS

334. The graphs of the quantities as functions of time are sine waves, with a phase displacement relative to one another (they are illustrated in Fig. 148 for the vibration $x = x_0 \cos \omega t$). The graph of the velocity as a function of the displacement is an ellipse, of the acceleration as a function of the displacement a straight line. If the amplitude of the displacement is x_0, the velocity amplitude is $v = \omega x_0$ and the acceleration amplitude $y_0 = \omega^2 x_0$, where ω is the angular frequency of the vibration.

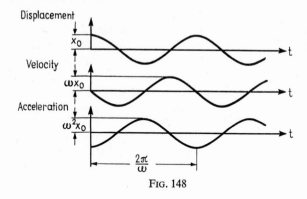

FIG. 148

335. $E_{\text{tot}} = \dfrac{1}{2}\,mA^2\omega^2,\quad E_{\text{kin}} = \dfrac{mA^2\omega^2}{4}\,(1 - \cos 2\omega t),$

$E_{\text{pot}} = \dfrac{mA^2\omega^2}{4}\,(1 + \cos 2\omega t).$

336. $T = \dfrac{4}{D}\sqrt{\dfrac{\pi m}{g\varrho}}.$

337. $T = 2\pi\sqrt{\dfrac{l}{g(\sin\alpha + \sin\beta)}}.$

338. The movement of the piston is given by

$$x = \frac{mgv_0}{S^2\gamma p_0}\left(1 - \cos S\sqrt{\frac{\gamma p_0}{mv_0}}\,t\right),$$

i.e. vibrations are obtained with the period

$$T = \frac{2\pi}{S}\sqrt{\frac{mv_0}{\gamma p_0}} \approx 0\cdot15 \text{ sec}.$$

339. (1) There is no difference; (2) the frequency is reduced, whilst the amplitude is increased. (For the diatomic molecules N_2, O_2 and H_2, $\gamma = c_p/c_v = 7/5$. For the monatomic gas He, $\gamma = 5/3$.)

340. Harmonic oscillation with the period $T = 2\pi\sqrt{R_0/g_0}$, where R_0 is the radius of the terrestrial sphere, g_0 is the acceleration due to gravity at the earth's surface.
Solution: The acceleration at a point distance r from the centre of the terrestrial sphere is $g_0 r/R_0$ if $r < R_0$, i.e. the acceleration is proportional to the displacement. The body therefore performs harmonic vibrations about the centre of the earth with amplitude R_0 and period $T = 2\pi\sqrt{R_0/g_0}$. (See Problem 292.)

341. (1) The block will gradually (as the acceleration increases) be displaced in a direction opposite to the acceleration; the maximum displacement is $\xi = ma/k \approx 1$ cm. (2) The block starts to perform vibrations given by $x = (ma/k)(1 - \cos\omega t)$, where x is the coordinate of the block relative to the trolley, measured from the initial position of the block, x being regarded as positive in the opposite direction to the trolley's acceleration; $\omega = \sqrt{k/m} \approx 9\cdot9\,\text{sec}^{-1}$. These vibrations are gradually damped because of friction and air resistance.
Note: When computing the displacement ξ and the frequency ω, the various quantities mentioned in the problem must be reduced

to the same system of units (c.g.s., m.k.s. etc.). This point should be remembered when solving other problems.

342. If the deflection of the block from the common centre of mass is x_1, and the deflection of the trolley x_2, we have $mx_1 = Mx_2$. The equation of motion of the trolley is

$$M\ddot{x}_2 = -(kx_2 + x_1);$$

on replacing x_1 from the previous equation, we get

$$M\ddot{x}_2 + k\left(1 + \frac{M}{m}\right)x_2 = 0.$$

Similarly, for the block,

$$m\ddot{x}_1 + k\left(1 + \frac{m}{M}\right)x_1 = 0.$$

The trolley and block therefore perform harmonic vibrations of frequency $\omega = \sqrt{k(m + M)/mM} \approx 10\cdot8$ sec^{-1}. The amplitude of the block vibrations is $lM/(M + m) = 5$ cm, of the trolley $lm/(M + m) = 1$ cm.

343. $T = \pi\sqrt{\dfrac{mL}{P}}$.

344. $x = \dfrac{P}{k}\left(1 - \cos\sqrt{\dfrac{kg}{P}}\,t\right)$.

The maximum tension in the spring is $2P$.

345. If the force exerted by the board on the load is $F' = -F$, the equation of motion of the load is $P - F' = md^2x/dt^2$. The load acceleration is found from the equation of its vibrations: $x = a\cos\omega t$; we have now $-F' = F = -P - ma\omega^2\cos\omega t = -(1 + 0\cdot32\cos 4\pi t)$ kg. We recommend that the graph of the variation of the force F with time be plotted.

346. $A > \dfrac{P}{m\omega^2} = \dfrac{g}{\omega^2} = \dfrac{9\cdot8}{16\pi^2}$ m. In the case of the limiting amplitude $A_0 \approx 6\cdot2$ cm the pressure of the load at the upper point becomes zero.

347. $k = \dfrac{4\pi^2 A}{gT^2} \approx 0 \cdot 1$.

348. $A = \dfrac{mg}{k} \sqrt{1 + \dfrac{2hk}{mg}}$.

349. $x \leqslant \dfrac{P}{k} = 20$ cm.

350. At resonance the friction force is equal to the external force and $F_{fr} = 100$ dyne. The velocity amplitude is $v_0 = A_{res}\omega = 20\pi$ cm sec^{-1}, $k = F_{fr}/v_0 = 5/\pi$ g sec^{-1}.

351. At resonance the phase of the velocity is the same as the phase of the external force and the amplitude of the velocity is a maximum, hence the work done by the external force in a period $A = \int f ds = \int_0^T fv\, dt$ is a maximum.

352. $T = 2\pi \sqrt{\dfrac{L}{3g}}$.

353. $T = 2\pi \sqrt{\dfrac{h}{2g}}$, where h is the height of the triangle.

354. $\dfrac{T_2}{T_1} = \dfrac{2}{\sqrt{3}}$.

355. $l = 15$ cm.

356. $\dfrac{T_A}{T_B} \approx 0 \cdot 9$.

Solution: Let x be the distance of the centre of gravity of half the disc from the disc centre, y the distance of the centre of gravity of the entire disc from its centre. Now, the moment of inertia of the half-disc relative to the axis through its centre of gravity is $J_0 = m(\frac{1}{2}R^2 - x^2)$, where m is the mass of the half-disc and R is the disc radius. The moment of inertia relative to the axis through the point A is

$$J_A = m_{\text{lead}}(R + x)^2 + m_{\text{lead}}\left(\frac{R^2}{2} - x^2\right) + m_{\text{al}}(R - x)^2 + m_{\text{al}} \times$$

$$\times \left(\frac{R^2}{2} - x^2\right) = R\left[m_{\text{lead}}\left(\frac{3}{2}R + 2x\right) + m_{\text{al}}\left(\frac{3}{2}R - 2x\right)\right].$$

The moment of inertia relative to the point B is

$$J_B = R\left[m_{\text{lead}}\left(\frac{3}{2}R - 2x\right) + m_{\text{al}}\left(\frac{3}{2}R + 2x\right)\right].$$

The vibrational periods are

$$T_A = 2\pi \sqrt{\frac{J_A}{(m_{\text{al}} + m_{\text{lead}})(R + y)g}} \; ;$$

$$T_B = 2\pi \sqrt{\frac{J_B}{(m_{\text{al}} + m_{\text{lead}})(R - y)g}} .$$

On taking account of the fact that

$$y = \frac{m_{\text{lead}} - m_{\text{al}}}{m_{\text{lead}} + m_{\text{al}}} x \quad \text{and} \quad \frac{m_{\text{lead}}}{m_{\text{al}}} = \frac{10}{2 \cdot 5} = 4,$$

we obtain $y = 3x/5$. Since $x = 4R/3\pi$, we have $T_A/T_B \approx 0.9$.

357. $T = 2\pi \sqrt{\dfrac{l\left[\dfrac{1}{3}\dfrac{\alpha^2}{\beta} + \left(1 + \dfrac{1}{2}\beta\right)^2 + \dfrac{1}{6}\beta^2\right]}{g\left(1 + \dfrac{1}{2}\beta + \dfrac{1}{2}\dfrac{\alpha^2}{\beta}\right)}} \approx 1.29$ sec,

where $\quad \alpha = \dfrac{b}{a} = 0.1; \quad \beta = \dfrac{\alpha}{l} = 0.1.$

Solution: $T = 2\pi \sqrt{J/Mgh}$, where J is the moment of inertia of the vibrating system, M is its mass, h is the distance of the point of suspension from the centre of mass. In our case

$$J = \varrho \left[\frac{1}{3} l^3 b^2 + \left(l + \frac{a}{2} \right)^2 a^3 + \frac{1}{6} a^5 \right],$$

$$Mh = \varrho \left[\frac{1}{2} l^2 b^2 + \left(l + \frac{a}{2} \right) a^3 \right],$$

where ϱ is the density of the material.

358. $\alpha_0' = \arccos \left(1 - \frac{l\omega^2\alpha_0^2}{3g} \right) \approx 8°$, where ω is the frequency of the oscillations of the pendulum prior to the load breaking off;

$$T = 2\pi \sqrt{\frac{2l}{3g}} \approx 1\cdot04 \text{ sec}.$$

Hint: At the instant when the load breaks off the rod has the angular velocity $\dot\alpha = \alpha_0\omega$, the kinetic energy $E_{\text{kin}} = J_{\text{rod}}\omega^2\alpha_0^2/2$, where J_{rod} is the moment of inertia of the rod. On equating this energy to the work done $\frac{1}{2}Mgl(1 - \cos\alpha_0')$ in raising the centre of mass of the rod to the point where it stops completely, we obtain the new amplitude.

359. The period will be the same as in the previous problem. The amplitude will be equal to the initial deflection of the pendulum, i.e. 10°.

360. Yes, the point is the centre of oscillation (percussion), which is $2l/3$ from the point of suspension. Attaching a load at the centre of oscillation of an ideal pendulum does not change its period, but the load dimensions must be very small compared with the distance from the centre of oscillation to the point of suspension.

361. *Solution:* The motion of the pendulum is given by $\alpha = \alpha_0\cos(\sqrt{3g/2l})\,t$. Newton's second law for the ring gives: $F - mg\sin\alpha = m\ddot\alpha d$, where F is the normal component of the required force, i.e. the normal pressure from the rod. Since $\sin\alpha \approx \alpha$, we have $F = m(\ddot\alpha d + g\alpha)$, and if we replace α, $\ddot\alpha$ from the equation of motion of the rod, we get

$$F = \alpha_0 mg \left(1 - \frac{3d}{2l} \right) \cos\sqrt{\frac{3g}{2l}}\,t.$$

The component Q of the required force tangential to the rod (the friction force) is obtained from

$$Q - mg \cos \alpha = m \dot{\alpha}^2 d.$$

Oh replacing $\cos \alpha$ by $1 - \frac{1}{2}\alpha^2$, we get

$$Q = m \left[g \left(1 - \frac{\alpha^2}{2} \right) + \dot{\alpha}^2 d \right]$$

or finally,

$$Q = m \left[g \left(1 - \frac{\alpha_0^2}{2} \cos^2 \sqrt{\frac{3g}{2l}} \, t \right) + \alpha_0^2 \frac{3gd}{2l} \sin^2 \sqrt{\frac{3g}{2l}} \, t \right]$$

$$= mg \left[1 - \frac{\alpha_0^2}{2} \left(\cos^2 \sqrt{\frac{3g}{2l}} \, t - \frac{3d}{l} \sin^2 \sqrt{\frac{3g}{2l}} \, t \right) \right].$$

362. $T = \pi \sqrt{\dfrac{L}{g}}.$

363. (1) If the two loads are moved in the same direction in the plane through the string clamping points, and through the same dis. tance, the period of vibration is $T_1 = 2\pi\sqrt{ml/F} \approx 0.05$ sec. (2) If the loads are moved through the same distance but in opposite directions, the period is

$$T_2 = 2\pi \sqrt{\frac{ml}{2F}} \approx 0.035 \text{ sec}.$$

(See the note on the answer to Problem 341).

Hint: In the first case the middle part of the string (between the loads) will always be parallel to its initial position, and it is only the tension in the extreme parts of the string that will communicate acceleration to the loads. The loads will therefore have the same motion as twice their mass situated at the mid-point of a string of half the length at the same tension. In the second case the mid-point of the string is at rest; each load therefore oscillates as though it were at the mid-point of a string of half the length.

364. If the maximum angular velocity $(d\varphi/dt)_{max}$ of the pendulum during its vibrations is less than the angular velocity ω of the shaft, i.e. $\omega - d\varphi/dt > 0$ at any instant, the moment of the friction force exerted by the shaft on the pendulum will always be in the same direction. Since this moment is constant, whilst the pendulum traverses the same path both in the direction of rotation and in the opposite direction during its vibrations, the work done by the moment of the friction forces during a period is zero.

365. During the vibrations the friction force exerted on the coupling-piece by the rotating shaft is in the direction of the motion of the pendulum during one half period, when the shaft and coupling-piece are rotating in the same direction, whilst the force is opposed to the motion of the pendulum during the other half period.

(1) If the friction force increases with the sliding velocity, it is greater in the half period when the coupling-piece and shaft are rotating in opposite directions. The work done by the friction force is therefore positive during a whole period, and the pendulum damping increases as a result of the friction between the coupling-piece and shaft.

(2) If the friction force diminishes with the sliding velocity, then on the contrary, for the same reasons, the work done by the friction force of the pendulum on the shaft is negative during a whole period, and the shaft communicates energy to the pendulum, so that the damping of the vibrations is diminished. In the case when the work done by the friction on the shaft is greater than the energy losses due to friction in the other parts of the pendulum, the energy of the pendulum oscillations will increase, the amplitude will increase, and the pendulum can perform self-oscillations.

366. The equilibrium position is displaced in the direction of the shaft rotation through the angle

$$\varphi_0 = \arctan \frac{\mu R}{a}.$$

§ 11. HYDROSTATICS AND AEROSTATICS

367. (1) Yes. (2) The equilibrium can be destroyed if the bodies undergo a different change in volume on submersion due to having different compressibilities. The compressibility is defined as $\Delta v / v \Delta p$, where Δv is the change in the volume v due to the pressure change Δp.

368. The weights must be made of the same material as the body being weighed.

369. $p = \dfrac{\pi}{6}\,[d_1^3(\delta_2 - \delta_1) + d_2^3\delta_1]\,g$.

370. $F = 1 \cdot 12$ kg.

371. (1) $\varDelta_1 Q \approx 400$ kg; (2) $\varDelta_2 Q = 196$ kg.

Hint: The hydrogen pressure in the balloon will also be practically equal to the external atmospheric pressure at a height of 2 km. Part of the hydrogen leaves the balloon via a valve. Knowing the weight of 1 m³ air at a height of 2 km, we can find the weight of 1 m³ hydrogen at the new pressure from the proportion

$$\frac{1}{1 \cdot 3} = \frac{x}{90}.$$

372. If the compressibility of the liquid (or gas) is greater than the compressibility of the body, it is possible in principle.

373. $P = H + \dfrac{h \times 10^3}{d}$ mm Hg.

374. $\delta = 1 - \dfrac{1}{n^2}$.

375. $F = \frac{1}{2}\,a^3\gamma$, where γ is the specific weight of water, $h = a/3$.

376. $P = 8 \cdot 64$ kg; $M = 41 \cdot 6$ kgcm.

377. $P = 34 \cdot 56$ kg; $M = 332 \cdot 8$ kgcm.

378. $P = h^2 \dfrac{c + 2d}{6} = 146$ ton.

379. $M = 210$ kg m.

380. *Solution:* We consider a belt 1 cm wide on the wall of the vessel, at a height of 1 m. There are no forces exerted in a horizontal direction by the parts of the wall adjacent to the belt, so that the liquid pressure forces are only balanced by the elastic forces of the belt. Let us consider an element of the belt of length $R\,d\varphi$, where R is the cylinder radius and $d\varphi$ is the angle. The ends of this element are acted on by forces from the adjacent elements that balance the pressure force $pR\,d\varphi$ on the element, i.e.

$$2F\frac{d\varphi}{2} = pR\,d\varphi.$$

F is the required stress. On substituting $p = 0\cdot4\ \text{kgcm}^{-2}$, $R = 1$ m, we get $F = 40\ \text{kgcm}^{-1}$.

381. $\varDelta p = 0\cdot017\ \text{kg cm}^{-2}$.

Hint: The following arguments can be used for solving the problem. We imagine dividing the balloon by an arbitrary diametral plane. The force $\varDelta p\pi R^2$ will act on each hemisphere. The hemisphere will be kept in equilibrium by the forces due to the fabric tension T, applied over the circumference of the great circle (in the section of the balloon by the diametral plane). This means that $\pi R^2\varDelta p = T2\pi R$, whence $\varDelta p = 2T/R$. On replacing T by its limiting value 850 kg m^{-1}, we can find the maximum permissible excess of the gas pressure in the balloon over the external atmospheric pressure.

382. $h \approx 5\cdot4$ km.

Hint: The pressure change dp is connected with the height change dh by $dp = -\gamma\,dh$, where γ is the specific weight of air. At constant temperature $p/\gamma = p_0/\gamma_0$. On substituting this in the previous equation and integrating, we get $\gamma = \gamma_0\exp\left(-\gamma_0h/p_0\right)$.

383. $\alpha = \arctan 0\cdot29 = 16°\,10'$.

384. $a = 4\cdot9$ m sec^{-2} when the acceleration is towards the more remote end, $a = 5\,g$ in the opposite direction.

385. There is no change.

386. The pressure on the front wall of the tanker is

$$P_1 = \frac{\varrho ah}{2}\left(gh + \frac{v_0^2l}{S}\right);$$

on the rear wall:

$$P_2 = \frac{\varrho ah}{2}\left(gh - \frac{v_0^2l}{S}\right).$$

§ 12. HYDRODYNAMICS AND AERODYNAMICS

387. $v = \sqrt{2gh} = 9 \cdot 8 \text{ m sec}^{-1}$.

388. $v = \sqrt{2g(h_1 + 0 \cdot 9h_2)} \approx 9 \cdot 5 \text{ m sec}^{-1}$.

389. $p = 2 \cdot 5$ cm of water column.

390. The point of intersection of the jets lies 25 cm below the second opening.

391. $Q = S_1 S_2 \sqrt{\dfrac{2g\Delta h}{S_2^2 - S_1^2}}$.

392. $h = \dfrac{v^2}{2g} = 5 \cdot 1$ m.

393. When the sailor brought the board up to the hole, the je bursting in acted on the board with a force $\varrho v^2 S = 2\varrho ghS$, where h is the height of the water column above the hole and S is the area of the hole. Once the board had covered the hole, the force acting on it was ϱghS, i.e. half as great.

394. (1) $\Delta p = \dfrac{\varrho v^2}{2} \approx 0 \cdot 06$ atm (ϱ is the air density). The ventilator produces rarefaction, and under the action of the pressure difference Δp the air acquires the velocity v in the pipe. (2) Due to viscosity, the pressure increases, because part of the pressure gradient is balanced by the friction forces.

395. $h = \dfrac{p_0}{\varrho g}$, where ϱ is the liquid density.

396. $F = \dfrac{\varrho Q^2}{S} \approx 40$ g.

397. *Solution:* The vertical speed of the jet at the water level in the glass is $v = \sqrt{2g(H - h)}$. The level in the glass rises by $\Delta h = Q/S$ per sec. The pressure on the bottom from the falling water is $\varrho Sv\Delta h$. The total pressure is $F = hgS\varrho + Sv\varrho\Delta h$, and t seconds after the start

$$h = \Delta h\, t = \frac{Q}{S}\, t,$$

$$F = \Delta h \varrho S[gt + \sqrt{2g(H-h)}].$$

Finally,

$$F = Q\varrho \left[gt + \sqrt{2g\left(H - \frac{Q}{S}\, t\right)}\,\right].$$

398. It is necessary to apply the force $F = 2S\varrho g(h_1 - h_2) = 0.5$ kg pushing the truck away from the top tap.

399. The balance reading drops by 12·5 g.

Solution: The water flowing from the hole acquires the momentum $\varrho v^2 S = 2\varrho ghS$ per sec. The water in the cylinder in turn exerts this force on the water in the jet. This means that the jet exerts an upward force $2\varrho ghS$ on the water in the cylinder. The vessel standing on the balance must therefore exert a force equal to the weight of the water minus $2\varrho ghS$ on the water at rest in the cylinder.

The reduction in the pressure of the water in the cylinder on its bottom is thus twice the previous pressure ϱghS of the water column at rest over the same area S.

400. The pressure on the cover falls by 72·5 kg.

Hint: The water flowing below the cover will acquire per second the momentum $\varrho Sv^2 = 2\varrho ghS = 72.5$ kg m sec^{-1}, i.e. the water in front of the cover will exert a force $72 \cdot 5$ kg m sec^{-2} on the jet flowing out. By Newton's third law, the jet will exert an equal and opposite force on the water in the channel (jet reaction).

401. We assume that, after striking the blade, the jet continues its motion with the blade velocity v_k. In this case the mass of water $S(\sqrt{2gh} - v_k)\varrho$ loses the velocity $(\sqrt{2gh} - v_k)$ per sec. The force acting on the wheel is therefore $F = S(\sqrt{2gh} - v_k)^2 \varrho$, and does work equal to $S\varrho(\sqrt{2gh} - v_k)^2 v_k$ per sec. The maximum is obtained when $v_k = \sqrt{2gh}/3$. The maximum power is therefore $4(2gh)^{3/2} S\varrho/27 \approx 8.75$ kg m sec^{-1} and the optimum angular velocity of rotation is

$$\frac{1}{3} \frac{\sqrt{2gh}}{R} \approx 2.2 \text{ sec}^{-1}.$$

402. $0\cdot047\,°C$.

403. If the kinetic energy of the jet, amounting to about 6 Joules per cm^3 water ($\approx 1\cdot5\,cal\,cm^{-3}$), were completely converted into heat, the jet temperature would rise altogether about $1°\cdot5$ as a result of striking the ice; this is clearly insufficient to explain the effect.

404. A paraboloid of revolution generated by the parabola $z = \omega^2 x^2/2g$, where x is the distance from the axis of revolution, z is the rise of the surface compared with its level at the centre of the vessel.

405. (1) $p = p_0 + \dfrac{\varrho\omega^2 R^2}{2}$, where p_0 is the pressure at the centre of the bottom, ϱ is the density of the water and R the distance from the centre of the bottom.

(2) $p \approx 42\cdot3\,g\,cm^{-2}$.

406. The cork is at the top on the axis, the lead is against the cylinder wall at the bottom, the body A is in any position (if its compressibility is equal to the compressibility of the water).

407. $T \approx 16\,g$.

408. The pressure difference communicates to each particle of the liquid a centripetal acceleration precisely equal to that necessary for the particle to move round a circle and not approach the axis of rotation.

409. (1) The liquid in the tube rises to the level at which the continuation of the surface of the paraboloid of revolution formed by the rotating liquid surface cuts the tube walls. The height of the liquid in the tube thus gives no indication of the pressure at the measurement end of the tube.

(2) Whatever the position of the end A, the liquid in tube D only rises to the level of the liquid on the cylinder axis, since the liquid in the tube CA is in rotatory motion. There will thus be a pressure gradient in the horizontal part CA of the tube, measured by the difference in heights above the point A and the centre. This method is thus also unsuitable.

(3) The height of the column in the tube D will be equal to the height of the liquid level above the end A. The pressure distribution can therefore be measured by this method.

410. The presence of the oil does not alter the shape of the water surface. The level in this case is 4 mm below the level referred to in the previous problem.

411. $F \approx 112 \cdot 5 \; \mathrm{g cm^{-2}}$.

412. Because a moment M, greater than the moment M_f of the friction forces, must be applied in order for the vessel to rotate uniformly. The work done by the moment $M - M_f$ goes into increasing the energy of the water, which is transformed into a flow from the centre to the periphery of the vessel A, and the energy of the falling water cannot be greater than this work. Consequently the work produced by the water wheel is insufficient to maintain the uniform rotation of the vessel.

413. The vessel must have the acceleration $a = 2g(H - h)/l$, directed to the right in Fig. 113.

414. The pressure drop due to friction in the part of the tube between the vessel and the first manometer tube must also be 5 cm; consequently the 3 cm head communicates kinetic energy to the liquid flowing in the pipe. This energy is equal to $\varrho g h = 2940 \; \mathrm{erg \, cm^{-3}}$, hence the liquid velocity $\approx 77 \; \mathrm{cm \, sec^{-1}}$.

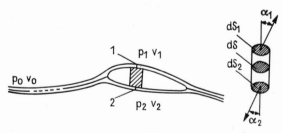

Fig. 149

415. *Solution:* Figure 149 shows the section of the infinitely long cylindrical body, the generators of which are perpendicular to the plane of the figure. The figure also shows the current tubes bordering the body, and the pressure p and velocity v close the three sections of the current tubes marked 0, 1 and 2. The section 0 is fairly remote from the body. Now, by Bernoulli's equation,

$$p_0 + \frac{\varrho v_0^2}{2} = p_1 + \frac{\varrho v_1^2}{2} = p_2 + \frac{\varrho v_2^2}{2}.$$

The force acting upwards on the small cylinder cut from the body
will be

$$(p_2 - p_1)\, dS = \frac{1}{2}\, \varrho(v_1^2 - v_2^2)\, dS.$$

The derivation uses the fact that $dS_1 \cos \alpha_1 = dS$ and $dS_2 \cos \alpha_2$
$= dS$, where dS_1 is the area of the upper surface of the cylinder, and
α_1 is the angle which the normal to this surface forms with the
vertical; the same for the lower face.

§ 13. ACOUSTICS

416. $x \approx 9\cdot6$ m.

Hint: The sound issuing from the point A reaches the man's ear
D in time τ (Fig. 150); in this time the bullet will be at the point C.

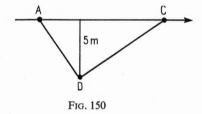

FIG. 150

The angle ADC is a right-angle, whilst AD is $340\,\tau$, $AC = 660\,\tau$,
whence the answer follows.

417. 10^{-3} sec.

418. The fundamental tone is apparently increased about 18 c/s,
the harmonic $n \times 18$, where n is the number of the harmonic.

419. 254 or 258.

420. Beats of frequency $2v_0 u/c$ will only be recorded by the receiver in the first case.

421. $v = 3400$ m sec^{-1}.

422. $N_k = k\,\dfrac{c}{2L}$, where c is the velocity of sound in the gas filling
the pipe, L is the length of the pipe, $k = 1, 2, 3, \ldots$ If the pipe is
filled with air the fundamental corresponds to $N_1 = 100$ c/s.

423. $N_{k+1} = \dfrac{2k+1}{4}\dfrac{c}{L}$; the notation is the same as in the previous problem. The fundamental corresponds to the frequency $N_1 = 50$ c/s, $k = 0, 1, 2, 3, \ldots$

424. See Fig. 151. The points 2 and 4 are displacement and velocity nodes and pressure antinodes, where the potential energy is a maximum (when $t = 0$, $t = \frac{1}{2}T$). The points 1, 3 and 5 are pressure

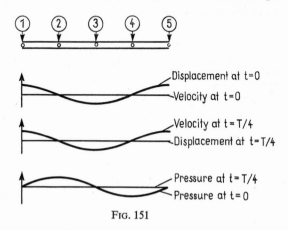

FIG. 151

nodes, and velocity and displacement antinodes, where the kinetic energy is a maximum (when $t = T/4$, $t = 3T/4$), T is the period of the vibrations.

425. $L = 30$ cm.

Hint: The frequency of the vibrations is $v = (1/2L)\sqrt{T/\varrho}$, where T is the string tension, ϱ is the mass of the string per unit length and L is the string length. The original length is found by using this relationship.

426. If

$$y_1 = a_1 \sin 2\pi\left(\frac{t}{T} - \frac{d_1}{\lambda}\right) = a_1 \sin(\omega t - \varphi_1)$$

represents the vibration of the particle, produced by the first wave system, and

$$y_2 = a_2 \sin 2\pi\left(\frac{t}{T} - \frac{d_2}{\lambda}\right) = a_2 \sin(\omega t - \varphi_2)$$

is the vibration produced by the second system, the total vibration will be

$$y = y_1 + y_2 = A \sin(\omega t + \psi),$$

where

$$A = [a_1^2 + a_2^2 + 2a_1 a_2 \cos(\varphi_2 - \varphi_1)^{1/2}$$

and

$$\psi = \arctan \frac{a_1 \sin \varphi_1 + a_2 \sin \varphi_2}{a_1 \cos \varphi_1 + a_2 \cos \varphi_2}.$$

427. The velocity of sound u is connected with the compressibility $\beta = -(1/v)(dv/dp)$ by $u = \sqrt{1/\varrho \beta_s}$ where ϱ is the density of the medium, v is its volume and p the pressure. We find for water: $\beta \approx 4{\cdot}35 \cdot 10^{-5}$ cm^2 kg^{-1}.

428. $\beta \approx 1{\cdot}35 \times 10^{-2}$ cm^2 kg^{-1}. Liquid helium is distinguished among other liquids, in particular, by its high comperssibility.

429. $c = v_0 2l = 1400$ m sec^{-1}. The overtones are $v_k = kv_0$, where $k = 2, 3$, etc.

430. The period of the thin string is half as long.

431. It must be reduced to one ninth.

432. The speed of sound in a gas depends on the ratio of the pressure to the density. Since this ratio is a constant at constant temperature, the velocity of sound is independent of the pressure.

433. The acceleration $f = 0{\cdot}1(2\pi)^2 \times 5^2 \times 10^8$ micron sec$^{-2} \approx 1000\ g$, the velocity $v = 0 \cdot 1 \times 2\pi \times 5 \times 10^4$ micron see$^{-1} \approx 3{\cdot}14$ cm sec^{-1}.

434. (1) Press the string over a very short piece at the middle; (2) press similarly at 1/3 the distance from the end. It is impossible to lower the tone of the string by such methods.

435. *Solution:* It follows from the equation of the adiabat that $dp/p = \gamma\, d\varrho/\varrho$. If y is the displacement of the particle in the wave, the relative compression is $-\partial y/\partial x$ and $d\varrho/\varrho = -\partial y/\partial x$. Consequently, $dp/p = -\gamma(\partial y/\partial x)$. On the other hand, if the displacement in the travelling wave is

$$y = A \sin\left(\omega t - \frac{2\pi x}{\lambda}\right),$$

we have

$$\frac{\partial y}{\partial x} = -\frac{2\pi A}{\lambda} \cos\left(\omega t - \frac{2\pi x}{\lambda}\right),$$

whilst the particle velocity is

$$u = \frac{\partial y}{\partial t} = A\omega \cos\left(\omega t - \frac{2\pi x}{\lambda}\right).$$

Hence

$$\frac{u}{c} = \frac{A\omega}{c} \cos\left(\omega t - \frac{2\pi x}{\lambda}\right) = \frac{2\pi A}{\lambda} \cos\left(\omega t - \frac{2\pi x}{\lambda}\right) = -\frac{\partial y}{\partial x},$$

i.e. $\dfrac{dp}{p} = \gamma \dfrac{u}{c}$.

436. (1) $v = 990/\pi \approx 315 \ \text{sec}^{-1}$;   (2) $c = 330 \ \text{m sec}^{-1}$;

(3) $\lambda = \dfrac{\pi}{3} \approx 1 \cdot 05 \ \text{m}$;   (4) $u = 99 \ \text{cm sec}^{-1}$;

(5) $\Delta p = \gamma p \dfrac{u}{c} = 1 \cdot 4 \times 760 \times \dfrac{0 \cdot 90}{330} \approx 3 \cdot 2 \ \text{mm Hg}$.

437. $u = \dfrac{v_1 \lambda_2 - v_2 \lambda_1}{\lambda_2 - \lambda_1}$; $\Lambda = \dfrac{\lambda_1 \lambda_2}{\lambda_1 - \lambda_2}$.

Solution: We seek the points x_1 and x_2 at which the phases of the two waves are the same at the instant t. The coordinates of the points must satisfy the equations

$$(\omega_1 t - k_1 x_1) - (\omega_2 t - k_2 x_1) = 0,$$

$$(\omega_1 t - k_1 x_2) - (\omega_2 t - k_2 x_2) = 2\pi,$$

where k_1 and k_2 are the wave numbers, equal to $2\pi/\lambda_1$ and $2\pi/\lambda_2$ respectively. Hence $\Lambda = x_2 - x_1 = \lambda_1 \lambda_2/(\lambda_1 - \lambda_2)$. The point at which the phases are the same will have the coordinate x_1' at the instant t', i.e.

$$(\omega_1 t' - k_1 x_1') - (\omega_2 t' - k_2 x_1') = 0,$$

whence the displacement velocity of this point is

$$u = \frac{x'_1 - x_1}{t' - t} = \frac{\omega_1 - \omega_2}{k_1 - k_2} = \frac{v_1 \lambda_2 - v_2 \lambda_1}{\lambda_2 - \lambda_1}.$$

438. $u = v_1 - d_1 \dfrac{v_2 - v_1}{d_2 - d_1}.$

439. $J = \dfrac{\Delta p^2}{2} \dfrac{S}{\varrho c} \approx 460 \text{ erg sec}^{-1} = 4 \cdot 6 \times 10^{-5}$ Watt.

Hint: The energy flux is $J = \frac{1}{2}\varrho u^2 cS$, and $u/c = \Delta p/\gamma p$ from the solution of Problem 435; knowing that the velocity of sound is $c = \sqrt{\gamma p/\varrho}$, we easily obtain the answer.

440. $A = \dfrac{u}{\omega} = \dfrac{1}{\gamma} \dfrac{\Delta p}{p} \dfrac{c}{\omega} \approx 2 \times 10^{-9}$ cm (see the solution of Problem 435; take the atmospheric pressure as 1013×10^3 dyne cm^{-2}).

441. $T = \dfrac{2\pi}{c} \sqrt{\dfrac{Vl}{S}}.$

442. The frequency of the vibration is increased $1/\sqrt{0 \cdot 069} \approx 3 \cdot 8$ times.